Enjoy your tonies

Your Sis

THE TRAIL OF
PAINTED PONIES

FROM FINE ART TO COLLECTIBLES

Anniversary Edition

Horse With
No Name
Loran Creech

THE TRAIL OF
PAINTED PONIES

Cover: War Pony by Rance Hood
Cover Photography: Darrell Kosechequetah
Cover Design: Bryn Wilkins & Karlynn Keyes

This book was conceived and published by:
The Trail of Painted Ponies, Inc.
P.O. Box 2629
Carefree, AZ 85377-2629
Phone: 480-459-5700
Fax: 480-361-5342

Visit our website at: www.trailofpaintedponies.com

Layout and Design: Karlynn Keyes & Bryn Wilkins
Written By: Rod Barker
Edited By: Bryn Wilkins & Karlynn Keyes
Design Assistants: Rikki Lodmell & Cindy Sutton

ISBN-13: 978-0-9760319-6-3

Library of Congress Cataloging-in-Publication Data

Artfully Printed in China by
Permanent Printing Limited
www.permanent.com.hk

FIRST EDITION

The Trail of Painted Ponies
FROM FINE ART TO COLLECTIBLES
Anniversary Edition

Welcome...

To The Trail of Painted Ponies
Anniversary Edition Book

*I*t has been seven years since *The Trail of Painted Ponies* rode into town. Seven being a lucky number, we felt it was an important time to publish an Anniversary Edition book on *The Trail of Painted Ponies*.

A book that tells the tale of *The Trail* from its beginning as an ambitious public art project, to its current status as the driving force behind a new American art movement and the source of one of the most beloved collectibles in America.

A book that functions as a collectors guide, providing *Painted Ponies* collectors with valuable and detailed information, available nowhere else.

A book that creates a greater understanding of *The Trail of Painted Ponies* phenomenon.

The selection of the horse as a medium for creative expression was an inspired idea. The horse isn't just any animal, but one that holds a special place in every American's heart. No animal is identified as closely with our history, our national character, our dreams, as the horse.

The horse has also been a source of artistic inspiration since the beginning of recorded history. From drawings on European cave walls, through the marble carvings on the Parthenon in Greece, to the Renaissance drawings of Leonardo da Vinci, the horse has been interpreted with endless variation and invention.

What *The Trail of Painted Ponies* has added, by giving contemporary artists the opportunity to imaginatively transform a blank horse sculpture into a unique and original work of art, is the versatility of the horse as a canvas. In the sense that every *Painted Pony* comes out of the same starting gate and crosses a different finish line, we are making our contribution to the long history of the horse in art.

With that, we invite you to saddle up and join us on a reading adventure along *The Trail of Painted Ponies*.

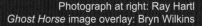
Photograph at right: Ray Hartl
Ghost Horse image overlay: Bryn Wilkins

The *Art of Horse Painting*

A UNIQUE, AMERICAN EXPRESSION

Spanish Explorers

When Spanish explorers "discovered" the Americas in the 1500s, there were no horses here. An earlier species that had once roamed the New World had been hunted into extinction. This explains the stunned reaction of the Native peoples when they first saw Conquistadors dressed in armor astride mounts covered in layered metal, parading into their villages. They thought some mythological creature had descended from the skies.

They quickly learned better. And in spite of the Spaniards' efforts to control access to horses in order to maintain the advantages it gave them in transportation, hunting and warfare – one of the first laws passed by the Spanish Conquerors forbid any Indians from riding a horse - the Native peoples soon recognized the power and promise of the horse, and adopted a "long-term loan without permission" policy.

Detail from: *Unity*
Original Life-size

Unity
George Monfils

Ghost Horse
Bill Miller (Mohican)

An Indian Horse Dance
Nebraska State Historical Society
Photograph Collections

A Gift from the Great Spirit

The acquisition of the horse had a profoundly transformative effect on most of the Indian communities in the American West. Within a century, horses had spread from tribe to tribe throughout "Indian Country," radically altering the traditional Indian way of life. Horses made traveling easier. Hunting ranges were expanded. The nature of warfare changed. Eventually, in most tribes, a person's wealth was measured in terms of the number of horses he owned.

Given the revolutionary impact of the horse on the Native nations, and their belief that horses constituted a sacred gift, it should come as no surprise that many tribes developed mythical stories that explained the origin of this "godsend," and even based religious ceremonies on the contributions the horse made to their lives. The step from there to painting and adorning the horse with colorful symbols and fantastic objects to endow it with magical powers was more than a manifestation of the artistic impulse of the American Indian to decorate natural objects. It was the birth of an art form whose recognition as an "American original" is long overdue, and deserves the status of an overlooked national treasure.

The Power of Paint

We have no way of knowing with certainty the exact beginning of the horse painting practice. We know that Indians had long incorporated symbols and designs into objects of both ceremonial significance and ordinary usage. We know that by the time the horse came along they had developed a variety of ingenious methods for applying color and adding accoutrements to different surfaces and materials for spectacular effect. And we know that for all it represented, the horse lent itself to glorification in the Indian way. For a people with a deeply felt sense of design and symbolism, it was only natural for the horse itself to become a medium for elaborate, creative expression, both artistic and mystical.

In the sketch below, a Cheyenne brave empowers his horse by painting it with different images. In honor of the dragonfly's ability to move rapidly in all directions, a skill that was useful in battle as well as on a buffalo hunt, he has drawn the image of a dragonfly on his mount's side. The circle around the pony's eye bestows great vision. Straight lines on the nose record coup (pronounced coo) counts, or enemies that he has killed.

The Power of Paint
Pen & Ink Sketch
Kevin Kilhoffer

Horse photograph Ray Hartl
Image overlay Bryn Wilkins

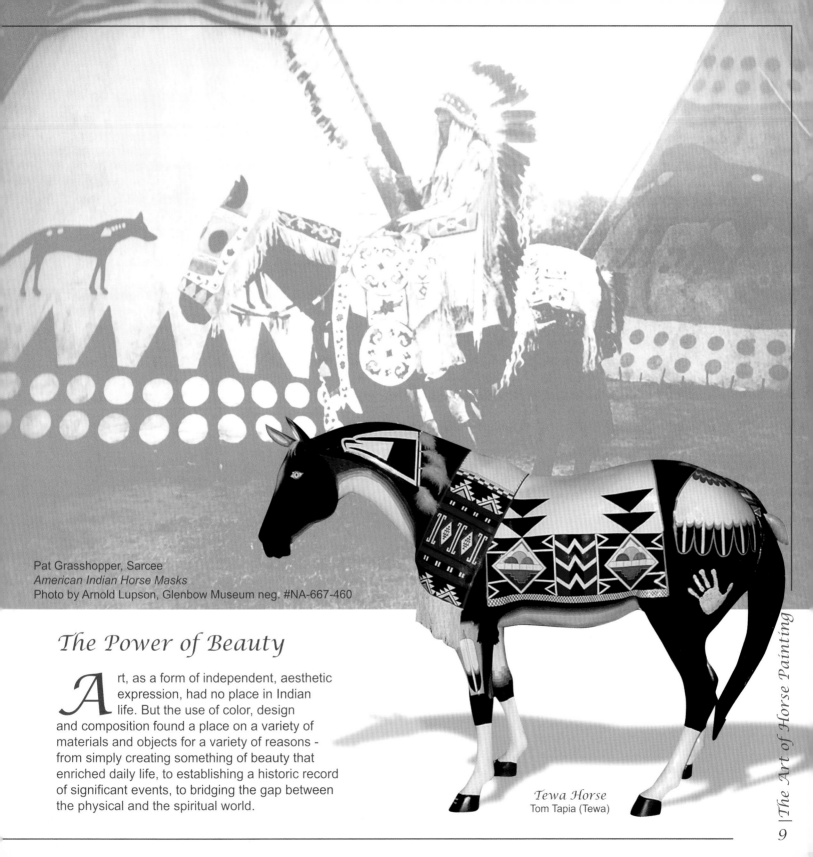

Pat Grasshopper, Sarcee
American Indian Horse Masks
Photo by Arnold Lupson, Glenbow Museum neg. #NA-667-460

The Power of Beauty

A rt, as a form of independent, aesthetic
expression, had no place in Indian
life. But the use of color, design
and composition found a place on a variety of
materials and objects for a variety of reasons -
from simply creating something of beauty that
enriched daily life, to establishing a historic record
of significant events, to bridging the gap between
the physical and the spiritual world.

Tewa Horse
Tom Tapia (Tewa)

Ledger Drawings

Because horse painting was a "perishable" medium, no concrete museum specimens have survived. We must depend on early buffalo robes and later, ledger-drawings for visual examples of the splendid ways in which Indian "artists" painted their horses. In the sense that most Indian "art" was functional as well as decorative, the colorful markings served a variety of purposes. When a warrior prepared to enter enemy territory, he would often paint symbols that told of his bravery in battle, and were intended to intimidate his adversary. Other designs told of dreams or visions and were believed to endow the horse with magical powers that would protect the rider.

New Bear Battle Scene
Gros Ventre Tribe, 1884
MSU - Billings Library Special Collections
Barstow Collection

Many Horses
Michael Horse (*Zuni*)

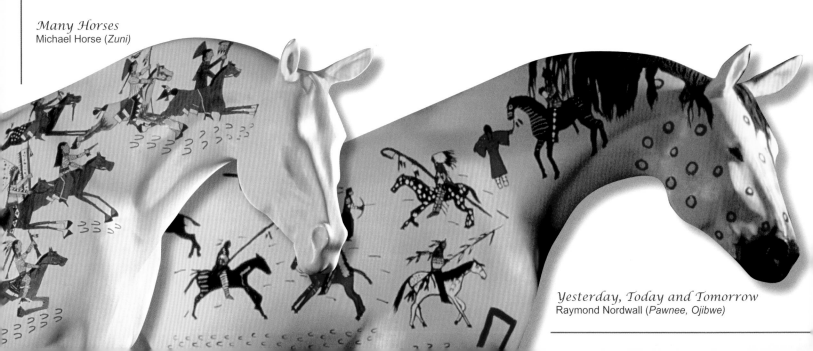

Yesterday, Today and Tomorrow
Raymond Nordwall (*Pawnee, Ojibwe*)

An Artistic Tradition

While different tribes developed unique symbols and colors for painting their horses, some markings were universal in their meaning. A red handprint on the horse's shoulder revealed that an enemy had been killed in hand-to-hand combat, and was the highest honor a warrior could achieve. A white circle painted around a horse's eye was believed to improve its eyesight. Add ornamental horse regalia - bridles, saddles and shields magnificently adorned with beads, feathers, fringes and porcupine quills - and you have a totally unique artistic expression.

Image above: Blackfeet Riders at the Calgary Stampede, 1912

War Pony
Rance Hood (*Comanche*)

War Pony
Original Life-size

Painted Ponies of Yesterday and Today

While the crucial role of the horse in the Plains Indians lifestyle ended in the 1870s, decorated horses continued to be an iconic figure in Native culture. Along with thunderbirds, Eagle feathers, sacred circles and handprints, the image of a painted horse retained its symbolic potency in Native arts and crafts. Elaborately dressed from bridle to tail with embroidered accessories, adorned horses were trotted out at parades, powwows and celebrations, often by Native women.

Ceremonial Pony
Cathy Smith

|The Art of Horse Painting

"Yellow Bull," 1900
Major Moorhouse Collection
Archives Center
National Museum of American History
Behring Center, Smithsonian Institution, 2987-B-14

Nez Perce Warrior

Major Moorhouse

*I*f there is one type of art that is authentically American, it is the art of horse painting. Horse painting as an art form, however, became a historically specific expression whose time had passed - until it was revived by *The Trail of Painted Ponies*.

The artwork generated by *The Trail of Painted Ponies* today is similar to the painted ponies of yesterday in many ways. *Painted Ponies* are also the manifestation of artistic impulses. *Painted Ponies* incorporate designs and symbols in ways that tell stories. Beneath the surface, there is magic at work. In short, *The Trail of Painted Ponies* honors and updates the distinguished aesthetic tradition and unique Native American art form of horse painting.

Runs the Bitterroot
Kevin Kilhoffer

The Tale of the Trail

FROM PUBLIC ART TO PHILANTHROPY

The Trail Begins

People looking at *The Trail of Painted Ponies* phenomenon might assume we began with a grand vision lighting the way; a road map spread out in front of us with a planned route to follow that led directly to a straightforward success story. But trails are rarely linear. Many are started without a specific destination in mind, just the belief in a direction. Trails that are covered on horseback in particular seem to involve journeys across a landscape of ups and downs. That's certainly true of the early trails that explorers and settlers followed into the American West. It's also true of *The Trail of Painted Ponies*.

When we started out in 2000 from Santa Fe, New Mexico – coincidentally the end of the legendary Santa Fe Trail, an important commercial trade route connecting Missouri and New Mexico in the 1800s – we began with an idea that was greeted with skepticism. In the months and years that followed, there were times when we wondered why we had taken the trail less traveled. But we spurred ahead… and with brush and paint in hand, and a horse sculpture we could call our own, we blazed a trail into an artistic frontier, creating a remarkable body of original artwork that has been honored by museum and gallery exhibitions, and has inspired one of America's favorite collectibles.

There is something special about trails, not the least because they often provide us with stories best told around a campfire. In the pages that follow you will hear an exceptional one. It is called, *The Tale of The Trail of Painted Ponies*.

You Can Lead a Horse to Water...

The new millennium did not start out well for New Mexico. A lack of snowfall in the high country leading to wildfires in the National Forest, and an economy that appeared to be running on fumes, were worrying businesses dependent upon summer vacationers to the Land of Enchantment. But Santa Fe journalist and author Rod Barker had a different perspective. He thought these were perfect conditions for an art extravaganza designed along the lines of a public art project that was doing wonders for Chicago. Featuring fiberglass cows whimsically painted by local artists, Cows on Parade™ in Chicago had brought millions of dollars into the local economy, as well as for charity. So Barker conceived of a similar event, with a Southwest spin.

The "vehicle" he had in mind was a horse. As a symbol of beauty, strength and freedom, the horse was truly an American icon. In the Southwest the horse was also a special part of history. From the Spanish Conquistadors who introduced the horse to North America nearly five centuries ago, to the Native Americans whose culture was transformed by the horse, to the cowboys who drove herds of cattle across these lands, the horse had been a working partner, a companion, a spiritual representative.

Barker also believed that there potentially could be broad interest in the artwork produced by such a project, if Santa Fe's world class art community got involved.

Likewise, as sparsely populated as New Mexico was, he thought it made sense to include multiple communities and showcase the range of talent that existed within New Mexico's borders. Being a state-wide project, he came up with the name: *The Trail of Painted Ponies*.

Paint-by-Numbers, a Maquette by Kevin MacPherson

24   25   26   27

Painted Pony Exhibition at the Governor's Gallery

Bidders line up at the first *Painted Pony* auction

Horsefeathers

The missing piece was an organization that would take on the responsibility of mounting the project. So Barker made a series of appointments with state and local arts agencies and organizations, fully expecting they would recognize the potential of the idea and adopt it as their own. To his dismay, they thought this was a gimmicky approach to public art, which was best left in the hands of professional arts administrators.

He decided to show everyone how it could be done by putting on a miniature version. He arranged for a local foundry to cast thirty-three one-foot-tall horses in a resin material. Then he personally started calling on artists in the community. Thirty-three agreed to paint a small *Pony*, and the results were astounding. There was a Pegasus with foot-long wings. A punk-rock *Pony* with a bristle-brush mane and wraparound titanium sunglasses. An "alien" *Pony* with a flying saucer attached to it that glowed in the dark.

After a two-week exhibition at the Governor's Art Gallery in the State Capitol in Santa Fe that set a record for attendance, an auction was held in a historic, downtown auditorium. It was what you would expect in the "City Different": lively and surprising. By the time the gavel came down to end the bidding, almost $50,000 was raised for the two beneficiaries: Challenge New Mexico, a therapeutic equine riding organization, and ArtSmart, a program that supported arts in the schools.

Surely, Barker thought, this would be proof enough that *The Trail of Painted Ponies* would be a winning project for the state of New Mexico, and an existing arts organization would take it on. But as the saying goes, you can lead a horse to water….

Fireman Pony
Dwayne & Ginger Ulibarri

Horse Flies
Ginger Lowry

Wound Up Time On The Range, a Maquette by Roger Evans

Cloud Prancer, a Maquette by Ron Olguin

28 29 30 31

Harold Sternfeld encourages bidders at auction

A volunteer helps bid up ponies at auction

Horse Flies
Ginger Lowry
Submission

Nature's Teasing
Del Lack
Submission

Sky of Enchantment
Ilse Magener
Submission

Hokusai's Great Wave
Mary Sweet

Nature's Teasing
Del Lack

Sky of Enchantment
Ilse Magener

HorsePower

*I*t was never Barker's intention to become "The Trailmaster," so to speak, of *The Trail of Painted Ponies*. He had no experience organizing and administering an art project. But by now he had also sold himself on the idea that this was something that ought to happen, one way or another. When no organization stood up he decided to form his own – HorsePower New Mexico – to assemble a team of dedicated, like-minded individuals, and to devote the next couple of months to promoting *The Trail of Painted Ponies* and see what happened.

In barnstorming style, he traveled the state like a politician in search of votes. The days were a blur of Kiwanis Club breakfasts, Chamber of Commerce meetings, Rotary luncheons, and cocktail receptions at the homes of wealthy art patrons, where he explained how the program worked. The idea was to bring communities, businesses and philanthropic organizations together in a mutually beneficial marketing partnership, he said, with art at the center. The partnership would be sponsorship-driven: corporations and businesses would sponsor a *Painted Pony* that would be; a) a tax-deductible advertisement for their business; b) a way of supporting a civic event that stimulated the local economy; and c) they had the right to select a philanthropic organization that would receive the net proceeds when, at the end of a public exhibition, the *Ponies* were rounded up and sold at auction.

Barker was proceeding under the assumption "If you build it, they will come." But there were moments during those months – a lot of them, he says – when he thought maybe he'd made a serious miscalculation. What kept him going were the *Ponies*.

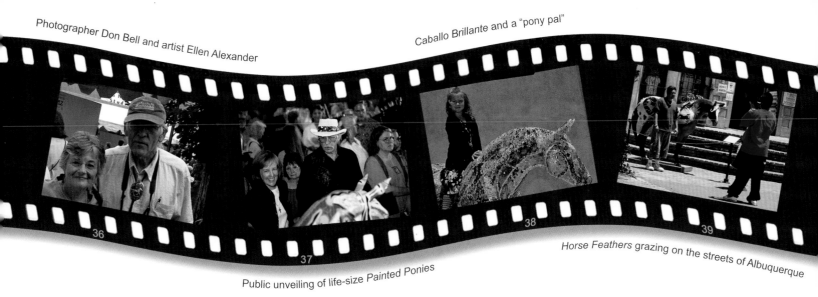

Photographer Don Bell and artist Ellen Alexander

Caballo Brillante and a "pony pal"

Public unveiling of life-size Painted Ponies

Horse Feathers grazing on the streets of Albuquerque

*I*n addition to issuing a general call through newspapers and magazines inviting artists to submit designs for imaginatively transforming a horse form into an original work of art, he had commissioned a nationally acclaimed Santa Fe sculptor, Star Liana York, to create an original horse form: a standing horse that possessed a dignified character in its own right, and at the same time, would serve as a source of inspiration to painters who would be asked to treat the horse as a canvas for personal expression. He had then recruited several celebrity painters whose names would not only lend the project prestige by association, but whose artistic styles, he thought, would translate fabulously onto a horse. Among them were Robert Rivera, the acclaimed gourd painter known for his Anasazi-style designs; JD Challenger, the artistic reincarnation of Buffalo Bill, famous for his indian portraits; and the actress/designer Ali MacGraw, who had traded her home in Malibu for an adobe in Santa Fe. Watching these artists at work and witnessing the way their paint brushes moved like magic wands on their Ponies, made all the difference. He realized that something amazing was being brought into the world. And that "something" translated into an optimism and it would only be a matter of time until everyone appreciated the special uniqueness of what was happening, and want to be a part of it.

Then, the phone started ringing. Calling, were people so charmed by what they'd heard about *The Trail of Painted Ponies* that they wanted to volunteer their help. Several art patrons phoned saying they wanted to commission a *Painted Pony* from their favorite artist, with the proceeds going to their favorite charity. Vindicating all that drive-time, art activists from towns outside Santa Fe – from Taos in the north to Carlsbad in the south, with points like Tucumcari, Roswell and Artesia in between – called to say they had been looking for an opportunity to put their towns on the New Mexico art map, what did they have to do to make sure *The Trail of Painted Ponies* paraded through their community?

Stacks of letters also appeared in the mailbox containing design submissions, and many were incredibly good. Sorting them according to theme, different "herds" took shape. There was the Native American herd, whose designs were inspired by the meaning of the horse to different tribes. A New West herd showcased modern interpretations of traditional cowboy themes. A Contemporary Art herd featured artworks by abstract painters and sculptors. A Spanish herd depicted our cultural and historic connection with Spain. But there were also highly stylized designs that simply could not be categorized… that looked like horses that might have escaped from some madcap circus traveling through the Southwest.

Across the land it was as if a spirit had suddenly taken hold… the spirit of *The Painted Ponies*.

Image at left: Original Life-size Standing Horse Sculptures

|The Tale of the Trail

Virgil Ortiz

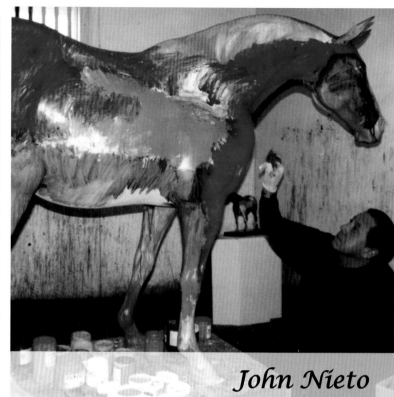

John Nieto

Noel Marquez

Ali MacGraw

BC Nowlin

Amado Peña

JD Challenger

Anne Sawyer

Thunderbird Suite
Joel Nakamura

Spirit War Pony
Tavlos

Sky Paint
Jim Alford

Pony Crazy

Barker had envisioned a project that featured fifty *Painted Ponies*. The forms were being cast in epoxy resin by a foundry in Albuquerque that could only produce a certain number in a given period of time. He had purchased a pickup truck and flatbed trailer and was personally delivering the five-foot by seven-foot horse forms to artists around the state. Everyone wanted to have the finished artwork installed and displayed in time for the summer tourist season. The timeline didn't allow for many more *Ponies*.

What he didn't factor in was that not only would more businesses than he anticipated embrace this innovative approach to marketing themselves while making significant contributions to their communities, but non-profit organizations would rise to the occasion. Rather than passively wait to be designated as a recipient, they were aggressively recruiting businesses to sponsor a *Pony* in their name.

Credit the media for this change of heart. National reports in major magazines and on network TV about the animal-themed public art wave that was sweeping the nation would cite *The Trail of Painted Ponies* as an example of this phenomenon. This piqued the interest of regional media, and feature articles about *The Trail* appeared in such publications as *Sunset Magazine, Business Art News, Sculpture, Southwest Art, Western Horseman, Cowboys & Indians,* and *AAA Auto Club's* magazine. Local newspapers followed suit. And virtually all the coverage was enthusiastic and positive.

Tracker
Daniel Morper

By the spring of 2001 things were happening so fast that Barker says, "We sometimes felt like passengers on a train that was picking up speed while track was being laid in front of us."

Fifty *Ponies*? By April, more than double that number were being painted, and HorsePower New Mexico was being pressured to add another ten or twenty *Ponies* in order to give more businesses, more artists, and more philanthropic organizations an opportunity to participate in and benefit from the project.

It is not an exaggeration to say that in the summer of 2001, New Mexico went "pony crazy". Vacationers arriving in New Mexico by airplane would walk down a gauntlet of surreal *Painted Ponies* installed at the Albuquerque Airport. Resorts and hotels throughout the state boarded *Painted Ponies* in their lobbies. The Department of Tourism Welcome Centers were stocked with brochures that promoted travel around the state and provided a map with the location of each community's "horse corral." The "giddy-up spirit" reached all the way to the United Kingdom, where a major newspaper sent a reporter to explore New Mexico via *The Trail of Painted Ponies*, and send back dispatches.

All this fanfare culminated in a toast from the Governor of New Mexico: "HorsePower New Mexico deserves a big thank you for their efforts in planning, organizing and realizing this event. The importance of independent projects, undertaken by enterprising young organizations that see an opportunity, take the initiative, and find a way to make it happen, cannot be overestimated."

SANTA FE

ot that there weren't bumps along the way. One night someone took a baseball bat to one of the *Ponies* on display in front of a business, leaving it in pieces on the sidewalk. This was the first real act of vandalism, and the reaction from the community is a testament to its affection for *Painted Ponies.* Citizens voluntarily donated money for a reward for information leading to the arrest of the vandal responsible. HorsePower New Mexico followed up by tacking up Wanted posters around town designed to remind people that at one time they lynched horse thieves. The guilty party was never found, and neither was another vandalized *Pony.*

What this incident did, was remind HorsePower New Mexico that the future was unpredictable, and that they should be on the lookout for something unforeseen that could derail the project. But as summer drew to a close and plans began to be made for a series of fall auctions, they couldn't imagine anything that would rain on this art parade.

The plan was to round up all the *Painted Ponies* into one space, exhibit them for a month or two, sell some directly to the public to establish their value, hold a series of live auctions at different locations, and then sell the remaining *Ponies* on the Internet through an online auction. In preparation, advertisements were placed in national magazines, promoting this one-of-a-kind "horse auction." Hotels offered special rates to people coming to New Mexico for the auction. Non-profit beneficiaries were given a tip sheet for building interest and value in their *Pony.* The excitement and buzz were building and it was only a matter of a couple of weeks before an auctioneer would open the bidding, when the unthinkable happened - America was attacked by terrorists - and the world it seemed, came to a stop!

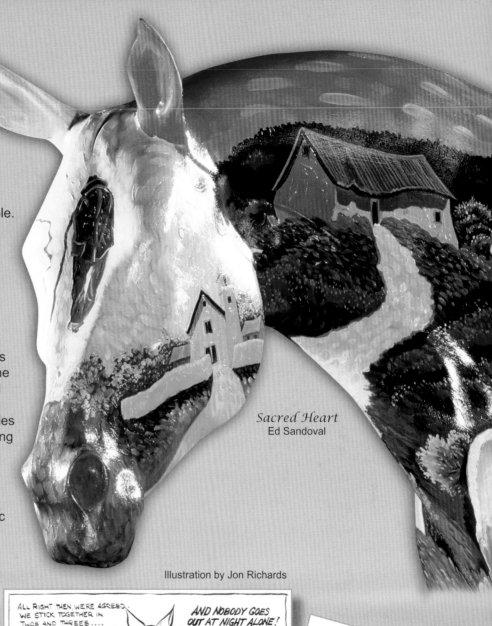

Sacred Heart
Ed Sandoval

Illustration by Jon Richards

|The Tale of the Trail

Going Once, Going Twice...

*I*n the days following September 11, 2001, the reaction to the World Trade Center tragedy was similar in Santa Fe to that in cities and towns across the country: people felt an overwhelming desire to make some gesture of sympathy towards the victims, and to express appreciation to those brave public servants who lost their lives responding to the call for help.

This led to a series of conversations in the HorsePower New Mexico offices about creating a special *Painted Pony* that memorialized the heroic conduct of the New York City Port Authority, firemen and policemen who had made the ultimate sacrifice. The resulting design was inspired by the memory of President John F. Kennedy's funeral procession in 1963, which was led by a riderless horse, ceremoniously dressed with a cavalry officer's saddle, with a pair of empty, high-topped boots fitted into the stirrups backwards. "The Fallen Heroes Memorial Pony" was a collaborative creation that became an instant shrine when it was unveiled before a crowd of several thousand people in Santa Fe on October 21, 2001.

While the creation of this "9/11 Pony" created a wealth of positive feelings, there were other conversations going on simultaneously in the HorsePower New Mexico offices that were sobering. They dealt with the fallout of 9/11 on the American mood and economy, and what this tragedy meant to the widely publicized plan to sell *Painted Ponies*.

The fires were still burning in the rubble of the World Trade Center when The Trailmaster made the decision to cancel the first *Trail of Painted Ponies* auction. He felt he had no choice. Civilian air travel around the United States had been suspended completely for days after the attack, and a state of high alert against potential follow-up attacks remained in place. People just weren't flying. Not only that, prospective *Painted Ponies* bidders were canceling their hotel reservations.

The second auction was scheduled for November 6, 2001, at the historic Lensic Performing Arts Center in Santa Fe, and as the date approached and it was apparent the country was still in shock, Barker was pressured to cancel it too. The auctioneer, who specialized in charity auctions, called and said that auctions elsewhere were postponing, and he recommended HorsePower New Mexico do the same. Executive Directors of several beneficiaries also voiced their opinion that people were not in the mood to buy big-ticket art objects, it was better to wait. But after considering the loss of momentum and potential consequences that could flow from a second cancellation, The Trailmaster felt the show had to go on.

Fallen Heroes Memorial Pony
The Trail of Painted Ponies

Auction
at the Lensic
Performing Arts
Center
Santa Fe, NM
November 2001

A catered reception on the Lensic Theater's stage preceded the auction, and a full house was in attendance. Before the bidding started it was announced that a pre-emptive offer of $45,000 had been made by a Dallas, Texas corporation for "When We Were As One," a stunning Native Pony painted by the Navajo artist Yellowman. That set the tone for the rest of the evening, as "Thunderbird Suite" by Joel Nakamura went for $17,000, "Caballitoscape a la Pena" by Amado Pena for $20,000, and "Ghost Horse" by Bill Miller for $22,500. A furious bidding war broke out over Lori Musil's sensational "CowPony" that brought the cheering crowd to its feet when it fetched $50,000 from the Booth Western Art Museum in Cartersville, Georgia.

The evening ended on a triumphant note when the auctioneer announced that in the last hour over a quarter-of-a-million dollars from the purchase of *Painted Ponies* had been raised for community associations, arts groups, health foundations, Indian art and culture organizations, schools, libraries, shelters, animal protection groups, and symphonies!

Images below, top to bottom:
Thunderbird Suite, Joel Nakamura
CowPony, Lori Musil
Caballitoscape a la Peña, Amado Peña

When We Were
As One
Yellowman

The Year of the Horse

The initial plan had called for the project to end with *The Trail's* End Auction. But when a tally was made and everyone realized the enormity of the economic and promotional impact that *The Trail of Painted Ponies* had on New Mexico, there was a public clamor for an encore.

This made sense for a number of reasons. Thanks to a hardback coffee-table book that had been published on the *Painted Ponies* and had quickly become a national best-seller, artists from around the country began sending in designs, expressing their desire to paint a *Pony*. Communities elsewhere in New Mexico were inquiring about how they could become part of *The Trail*. National non-profit organizations were submitting proposals for marketing partnerships. And then there was the matter that a number of the original *Ponies* remained unsold. Extending the project to a second year would lengthen the selling season.

Taking all these things under consideration, it was decided that if HorsePower was going to mount a creative sequel there needed to be an energizing concept that enlarged and broadened the original idea of a public art project. With that in mind they came up with an initiative that was presented to the Governor of New Mexico, who thought it was a winner.

New Mexico Governor
Gary Johnson

Bottom Row, From Left to Right:
Year of the Horse, Lori Musil; *Run for the Roses*, Janee Hughes; *Renewal of Life*, Natasha Isenhour; *Five Card Stud*, Gerri Mattson

Proclamation by Governor Gary Johnson Proclaiming
"The Year of the Horse"

On February 12, 2002, the first day of the Chinese "Year of the Horse," Governor Gary Johnson issued a proclamation declaring 2002 the "Year of the Horse" in New Mexico. Immediately following, the Office of Cultural Affairs put out a press release announcing it was organizing a series of equine exhibits in several state-operated museums. Included were the Museum of Natural History and Science in Albuquerque (which would display fossil remains of the horse that roamed North America in ancient geological times); the Museum of International Folk Art in Santa Fe (where an exhibit would be mounted displaying tack and gear worn by the horses belonging to Spanish explorers); the Museum of Indian Arts & Culture in Santa Fe (where a tribute to the Native Art of Horse Painting would be exhibited); and the New Mexico Farm and Ranch Heritage Museum (which would present a historical retrospective of horse-drawn equipment). Also supporting the effort to elevate New Mexico's profile as a "horse state" would be a series of activities and events put on by equine-related businesses, facilities and activities… and leading the charge with a new running horse form for artists to paint was *The Trail of Painted Ponies*.

In 2002, *The Trail of Painted Ponies* expanded to include more communities and participation by national non-profit organizations. Bringing national attention was an invitation to display the "Fallen Heroes Memorial Pony" in the Central Terminal at La Guardia Airport in New York City on the first 9/11 anniversary. All these festivities culminated in a second Trails End Auction that was highlighted by the purchase of "Five Card Stud," along with three other life-size *Painted Ponies*, by the legendary country-and-western music star and co-host of the TV show "Hee-Haw," Buck Owens.

Clockwise from Top Left:

King Tut's Royal Trotter
Steven Alverson
Tightly Woven
Pat Beason
Painted Pony in Garciavision
Rick Garcia
Five Card Stud
Gerri Mattson
Blondes
David DeVary
Desert Dream Horse
Ellen Alexander
Lady Ledoux
Inger Jirby
Muy Caliente
Pat Beason
New Mexico Sun Magic
Storm Townsend
Snow Pony
BJ Briner
Turbo Hay Burner
Brett Chomer

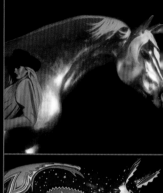
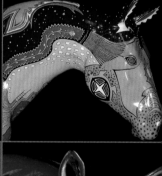

Counter-clockwise from Top Right:

Jackson's Jazz
Dianne Schiles
Wilderness Roundup
Mitzie Bower
Wildfire
Gerri Mattson
Boot Scootin' Horsey
Carla Slusher
Dances with Hooves
Ty Anderle
Sabanilla Bella
Fredrico Vigil
Karuna
Ali MacGraw
Rosie the Apparoosa
Marianne Hornbuckle
Horsepower to Burn
Rich Mattson
Special Gift Horse
Kay Brubaker
Pony Tales
Fran Larsen

A unique project in New Mexico triggers a revolution in equine art.

Article by Karin Hawkins
Photographs Courtesy HorsePower New Mexico

WHEN SOUTH AFRICAN traveler Rena Leroux made her way off the escalator at Albuquerque's International Sunport in August 2001, she nearly dropped her carry-on bag. "There's...

HorsePower New Mexico uses 'Compassionate Capitalism'

BY R. LYNN BARNES | SPECIAL TO NMBW

Rodney Barker doesn't think of himself as a philanthropist. He calls himself an entrepreneur, but you'd be hard-pressed to find another entrepreneur who gives 80 percent of his revenue to charity. Last year he raised more than $500,000 through **HorsePower New Mexico**, a limited liability corporation that organizes public art events. That money — raised despite the economic downturn and Sept. 11 — was given to 40 charitable organizations in New Mexico. Barker used a concept called compassionate capitalism — designed to make a profit, but dedicated to the greater good.

More businesses are taking that kind of philanthropic risk so they can participate in the community as corporate citizens. As the compassionate capitalism model emerges, businesses are becoming more aware of their role in co...

others. Those had a similar goal – to raise money for charities while stimulating the local economy – and were all organized by city governments with their accompanying resources. But neither Santa Fe nor Albuquerque wanted to take the risk and invest in the project.

So Barker developed a variation of the public art project as a win-win enterprise. As a successful investigative journalist, he had writ...

INTRODUCING

Philanthropy
IN THE SOUTHWEST

The Trail of Painted Ponies

Inside

SITE Sante Fe

National Dance Institute of New Mexico

Extended Coverage of the Southwest

|The Tale of the Trail

Philanthropy

As the "Year of the Horse" came to an end and people took stock of the difference *The Trail of Painted Ponies* had made to so many lives, expressions of appreciation rolled in. "Thank you so much for your gift of $32,000, our share of the proceeds from the sale of a beautiful *Painted Pony*,'" wrote the Executive Director of The Food Depot. "Your gift will enable us to provide more than 100,000 meals to people in need in our community… please accept our gratitude for the important part you played in the fight against hunger." "It was with a great deal of appreciation that Santa Fe Habitat for Humanity received checks totaling over $52,000," wrote the co-chair for fundraising. "I can assure you that this event was not only our most profitable project, but also the most enjoyable." More than one organization agreed with the Director of Casa Esperanza who wrote, "With the terrible events of September 11, 2001, the non-profits of New Mexico have experienced a great reduction in their financial support. Your project may very well allow some non-profits to continue to exist and care for those who are in need of their services."

New Mexico's premier public art project brings the mythology and dignity of the horse to the Land of Enchantment.

BY ROBIN HENDRICKSON

Imagine entering the Albuquerque airport and having six wildly adorned life-size model horses greet you. Throughout most of 2001, that's exactly what visitors encountered when deplaning at New Mexico's major port of entry. For many, it was their first glimpse at HorsePower New Mexico's Trail of Painted Ponies.

The Trail of Painted Ponies brought together artists, businesses and charities in what is possibly New Mexico's most successful public art project. Envisioned by Rod Barker and driven by project sponsor HorsePower New Mexico of Santa Fe, the project went from an idea to raising $500,000 for New Mexico charities.

The focus of the project is threefold: to showcase New Mexico's world-class art community, to provide businesses with an innovative way to market themselves and to raise funds for New...

Trailblazing

*T*he *Trail of Painted Ponies* was the largest public art project in the history of the state of New Mexico. At the same time it paid tribute to that uniquely American tradition of horse painting, it generated a body of artwork the likes of which had never been seen before. *Painted Ponies* had been incorporated into the prized collections of art patrons, and were showcased in corporate lobbies and museums across America.

As for what lay ahead, there were some who wondered if *The Trail of Painted Ponies* would ride into the sunset, leaving behind a proud legacy of benefits and memories. But the fact of the matter was that out of the success of the past, a vision for the future had emerged. A vision of expanding to new ranges, and continuing to blaze new trails.

Trevi Fountain, Rome

Marble Masterwork

From Masterworks to Masterpieces

At the same time *The Trail of Painted Ponies* was updating the distinguished American tradition of horse painting "pioneered" by Native Americans, it was breaking boundaries in the world of contemporary art by redefining the notion of canvas, in the artistic sense of the word. Until this time, the traditional canvas was a square cloth painted, framed and hung on the wall. *The Trail* was giving artists a dynamic, three-dimensional form to paint that was animated with life and energy... charged with associations - psychological and historic - before a single brushstroke was applied... whose proportions and profile changed as you moved around it.

At the conclusion of the public art project, the interest in *Painted Ponies* was so extraordinary that *The Trail* decided to continue to create opportunities for artists to explore this new dimension in art and give them a smaller more precious form to paint. Called "Masterworks," they stood two feet tall, were marble-cast and presented the horse in an alert and dignified walking position.

The Trail then announced plans to host a series of national art competitions to broaden the scope of *The Trail of Painted Ponies*.

The Native Art of Horse Painting Competition

*T*he first competition, "The Native Art of Horse Painting," invited contemporary Native artists as well as non-Native artists to submit designs that expressed the unique history, experiences and traditions of Native Americans on the form of a horse, just as Native warriors once did.

Personal invitations to participate were sent to every registered tribe in America. *Southwest Art Magazine*, one of the premiere fine art magazines in the country, signed on as a media partner and ran full-page ads in its magazine. Media across the country printed announcements about the competition. And out of over 600 submissions, a panel of distinguished judges selected twenty finalists to paint Masterworks.

After the Ponies were painted they were photographed and America was given the opportunity to vote for its favorite on *The Trail of Painted Ponies Official Website*. More than 12,000 votes were cast, and the top vote-getters were announced at a gala in a ballroom at the Four Seasons Resort in Scottsdale, Arizona.

It was an event to remember, and was organized similarly to the Academy Awards Ceremony. Before announcing the winner, The Trailmaster said, "Television has its Emmies. Broadway plays have their Tonys. The music industry has its Grammies. From this night forward there will be a new and equally prestigious award ceremony for visual artists called, 'The Ponies.'" He then invited all twenty finalists to join him on the stage, because on this night they were all winners.

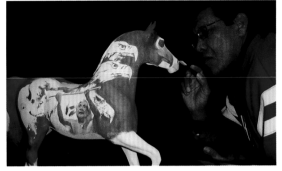

Sacred Paint
Gary Montgomery
Competition Finalist

Fancy Dancer
Devon Archer
People's Choice Award Winner

Native Art of Horse Painting Top 20 Finalists Awards Ceremony
Four Seasons Resort, Scottsdale, Arizona

America The Beautiful Competition

So successful was "The Native Art of Horse Painting" that *The Trail* followed up with a second national art competition, titled "America the Beautiful." A call went out to artists across the country to submit original and imaginative designs in three categories: The American West, Americana and the Spirit of America. Once again, the response was overwhelming. Ten new Masterworks were created, which not only dramatically demonstrated the diverse subject matter that the horse could accommodate, but attracted the attention of the media, art critics, and museum directors who expressed an interest in mounting *Painted Ponies* exhibitions.

Canyon Beauty
SJW Grogan

Morning Star and Stripes
Leslie Gates

Signs of the Times
S.V. Medaris

Canyon Beauty
SJW Grogan

For Spacious Skies
Janet Snyder

Signs of the Times
S.V. Medaris

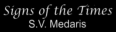

Bunkhouse Bronco
Lynn Bean

Carved in History
Chad Brady

The Greatest Generation
Laurie Holman

Southwest Silhouette
Aloma Wolfington

Merry-Go-Round America
Lexie Palmore

Stars and Stirrups
Kevin Kilhoffer

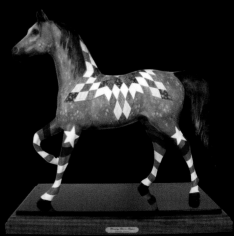

Morning Star and Stripes
Leslie Gates

Native Art of Horse Painting Exhibition
Booth Western Art Museum

The Booth Western Art Museum in Cartersville, Georgia, was the first museum to feature a *Trail of Painted Ponies* exhibition. In the winter of 2006 it featured the winning sculptures in the "Native Art of Horse Painting" competition. In conjunction with the opening it hosted several *Painted Ponies* artists who spoke to an admiring crowd about the challenges a "three-dimensional" canvas presented, and how they had turned this into an opportunity to "paint outside the lines."

An invitation from another prestigious museum immediately followed.

Booth Western Art Museum
Cartersville, Georgia

Sounds of Thunder
Bill & Traci Rabbit

The Trail of Painted Ponies Exhibition
Booth Western Art Museum

Competition Finalist Kevin Kilhoffer with Collector
Booth Western Art Museum

Competition Finalist Denise Brown and Collectors
Booth Western Art Museum

The Tradition of Excellence

Trail of Painted Ponies Exhibition
International Museum of the Horse

The profile of the International Museum of the Horse in Lexington, Kentucky had been recently elevated by two history-making exhibitions: "The Art of the Horse in Chinese History," and "All the Queens Horses: The Role of the Horse in British History." A third major exhibition was held over the summer of 2007 which introduced a new American Art Movement. It was launched with the public unveiling of the spectacular sculptures from the "America the Beautiful" competition, along with the announcement that a new "ism" was being introduced to the contemporary art scene. One that introduced horse and art lovers not only to a totally different way of enjoying the horse in art, but "Art" itself. The name? *Pony Expressionism*, from *The Trail of Painted Ponies*.

The Magician
Andersen Kee

Crazy Horse
CJ Wells

Journey of Aspen Winter
Mark Silversmith

Ceremonial Pony
Cathy Smith

Detail From: *Southwest Silhouette*
Aloma Wolfington

Continuing The Tradition

The summer-long, "Pony Expressionism" exhibition at the International Museum of the Horse brought a new prestige to *The Trail of Painted Ponies*.

Not long ago a New York Times art critic lamented, "We are in a lull and no artist is making very large or very deep changes in our sense of what sculpture can and should do. But who knows? Any day now the next big thing could hit, opening up a brave, new three-dimensional world." In the way *The Trail of Painted Ponies* had created a new artistic medium which showcased the versatility of the horse as a canvas that can accommodate a powerful range of artistic expressions, it was opening up that "brave, new, three-dimensional world."

Were that to be all that *The Trail of Painted Ponies* accomplished, it would be significant enough. But, *The Trail* did not end there. It took its art to another level. It took it out of the Museums and onto Main Street when it decided to craft small-scale replicas of the original *Painted Ponies* that captured their beauty and wonder with such grace that they would become highly collectible, miniature works of art themselves.

The World of Collectibles

The Stampede Begins

What began as a Santa Fe-based public art project had undergone a change of focus in 2003, when the organization behind *The Trail of Painted Ponies* dropped the name HorsePower New Mexico, and moved its headquarters to Arizona.

"We felt at home on this range," said the Trailmaster, pointing out that Arizona was home to the remaining bands of Spanish horses brought to this country almost 500 years ago, as well as a state known for its support of art and culture. The year that followed was good for *The Trail*:

1) A full-length documentary film on *The Trail of Painted Ponies*, narrated by actress Ali MacGraw, premiered at the Santa Fe Film Festival. The accolades it received carried all the way to Public Television in New York, the 4th largest PBS station in the country, who picked it up to headline its August 2003 pledge week.

2) The move introduced *The Trail* to Double Star Studio, owned by art/business consultant Karlynn Keyes, who arranged a series of major Arizona *Painted Pony* exhibitions. Over the following months, life-size *Painted Ponies* were displayed in the rotunda of the Arizona State Capitol; headlined the Arizona Sun Circuit Quarter Horse Show; welcomed VIP dignitaries at the JW Marriott Hotel crown jewel, the Camelback Inn; graced the lobby of the Dodge Theatre, the premiere performance center in downtown Phoenix; celebrated the 50th anniversary of the Parada del Sol, the nation's largest horse parade; supported the Scottsdale Symphony Orchestra; and themed the Oasis Gift Show, the Southwest's largest trade show.

3) Maintaining a charitable dimension to its activities, *The Trail of Painted Ponies* also found time to partner with Sunland Park Racetrack & Casino in El Paso, to put on a *Painted Ponies* exhibition and auction benefiting a Las Cruces, New Mexico non-profit organization that provided child care to homeless families, Jardin de los Ninos. Over $120,000 was raised, bringing *The Trail of Painted Ponies* total philanthropic contribution to close to a million dollars.

Award-winning Documentary   Arizona State Capitol   Dodge Theatre   JW Marriott Event   Sunland Park Racetrack   Oasis Giftshow

*B*ut without question, the most significant development to take place in 2003 was the one that launched *The Trail of Painted Ponies* into the world of collectibles.

In the early days, *The Trail of Painted Ponies* merchandise had been limited to a poster and a T-shirt sold at *The Trail's* offices. Then, in the fall of 2001, it had published the first *Trail of Painted Ponies* book, which contained pictures of all the Ponies in the original public art project. The book was perceived by some to be a catalog, and *The Trail* received numerous inquiries from people interested in buying miniature replicas of the *Painted Ponies* pictured in the book. Recognizing a good idea when he heard it, the Trailmaster began a search for a manufacturing company of collectible figurines.

Paramount in importance was the company's ability to craft a high-quality collectible that captured the beauty and magic of the original *Painted Ponies*. When that company was found, a licensing agreement followed that led, less than a year later, to the 2003 Atlanta Gift and Decorative Accessories Show. It is the largest gift and collectible show in the industry, and where *The Trail of Painted Ponies* figurines were first introduced to the buying public.

Twelve *Painted Ponies* had been produced and each stood approximately 6 inches tall. They were arranged on a small table top in a crowded showroom among an assortment of other collectibles. To make sure no one could miss them "Motorcycle Mustang," a life-size *Painted Pony* from the public art project, had been delivered from New Mexico to provide context. It stood beside the display like some protective big brother who had come along to watch over the little ones.

It also served as a point-of-purchase attraction, though as it turned out, that wasn't really necessary. *Painted Ponies* figurines stopped buyers in their tracks. To say they were a hit would be an understatement.

Motorcycle Mustang
David Losoya

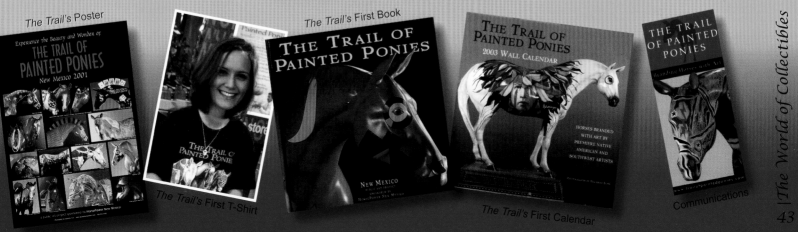

The Trail's Poster

The Trail's First T-Shirt

The Trail's First Book

The Trail's First Calendar

Communications

| |
43
The World of Collectibles

Miniature Works of Art

*T*o some extent the overwhelmingly positive response to *Painted Ponies* figurines can be credited to the fact that horses are an icon. Any collectible that paid tribute to the horse in a wholly different and fabulously colorful way was bound to receive a certain amount of attention. But that doesn't begin to explain the extraordinary appeal of *Painted Ponies*. The following would need to be taken into consideration:

The three forms - a standing horse with just enough body language to give it life; a running horse that captured the liberated spirit of a horse galloping across the plains; and a walking horse that conveyed majesty. Created exclusively for *The Trail*, they were sculptural artworks in their own right, which meant every *Painted Pony* was an example of art-on-art.

The original artwork - the ingenious and visually thrilling ways the original *Painted Ponies* combined art, thought and culture set them apart. Add the exquisite craftsmanship and attention to detail that had gone into creating the figurines, and the magic of scaling down the form and successfully compressing the original designs, and you have essentially decoded their appeal. *Painted Ponies* figurines were instantly recognized as miniature works of art.

This had not come about accidentally. Any attentive survey of the collectible landscape will reveal the market calculation that goes into the production of a lot of collectibles. Many are designed with hearts and handbags in mind.

But there was an authenticity and sincerity to the *Painted Ponies* that not only made them unique, but somehow seemed to give each and every one a soul.

Anasazi Spirit Horse
Robert Rivera
6" Figurine

Anasazi Spirit Horse
Robert Rivera
Original Life-size

The Number One Collectible In America!

With the release of *Painted Ponies* collectibles into the marketplace, "Discover the Beauty and Wonder of *The Trail of Painted Ponies*" became more than just a slogan. It described something that was happening across the country. Within a year, *The Trail of Painted Ponies* figurines were one of the fastest selling collectibles in America.

Not only were *Painted Ponies* carried by traditional gift and specialty stores, they filled the windows in airport and hotel gift shops, and graced the shelves of Hallmark Stores everywhere. Their appeal was so broad that they were sold in places you would never expect to find a collectible: art galleries, jewelry stores, florist shops, boutique pharmacies, not to mention western clothing and tack and feed stores. Retailers couldn't keep them in stock. Something of a coronation took place when the gift industry trade publication Giftbeat Magazine polled stores around the nation and listed *Painted Ponies* as the #1 collectible in America!

Artists Robert Rivera, Bill Miller and a Delighted Collector

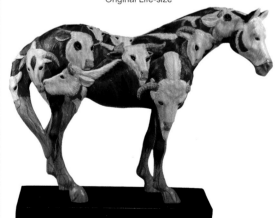

CowPony
Booth Western Art Museum
Collectors Randy & Jackie Thompson
Original Life-size

It wasn't long before merchandisers took note of this rapidly rising brand and began to approach *The Trail* with licensing offers. Some of the overtures were turned down with little consideration because *The Trail* was intent on preserving its reputation for artistic excellence. When it did sign a licensing agreement the intention was to give people different ways of enjoying *The Trail of Painted Ponies*.

Far and away, however, the collectible that delighted collectors the most was the exquisitely crafted *Painted Ponies* figurines. People weren't just buying one or two, but carefully acquiring collections. Many began a quest to purchase them all.

CowPony
Lori Musil
6" Figurine

It was apparent to everyone connected to *The Trail of Painted Ponies* that something unusual was happening. Every year, millions of dollars were spent by large companies in an attempt to develop collectible products that would catch fire with consumers. Millions more were spent on promotion and advertising. But, with a very small regional promotional push, depending primarily on the world's oldest information highway... word-of-mouth... *Painted Ponies* figurines were touching lives, filling a void.

*I*n an attempt to understand the basis of their appeal to collectors, *The Trail* turned to collectors on its official website. Originally designed during the public art phase as a place where people could come to view and bid on life-size artworks, www.trailofpaintedponies.com had evolved into a news magazine. It was updated monthly with the latest information about the figurines, and feature stories about activities and events along *The Trail*. It was also an interactive website, which led to the question: Why do you think *Painted Ponies* are the Hottest Collectible in America?

The feedback was better than anything that could have come from a focus marketing group. Of the hundreds of responses, ten stood out:

1) *Painted Ponies* can match all your different moods. Feeling fearful? "War Pony" will give you strength. Money on your mind? "QuarterHorse" is the horse for you.

2) *Painted Ponies* are inexpensive. They don't cost a fortune to keep, and guess what? Hold on to them long enough and they will increase in value!

3) *Painted Ponies* can combine two hobbies in one. If you love horses and love playing cards, you'll love "Five Card Stud." Or if you love motorcycles, "Motorcycle Mustang" is the perfect *Pony*.

4) *Painted Ponies* let you live out experiences you may have missed. "Route 66 Pony" takes you for a trip down the Mother Road. If you've never seen a forest fire blazing through the woods, "Wildfire" will show you what it's like.

5) *Painted Ponies* give you feelings you want to share with others. This is why they make such wonderful gifts for people who are special to you

6) *Painted Ponies* inspire us to remember our childhood dreams… our first ride on a carousel…playing in the garden when young… the first time I was in the presence of a real, live, warm and mysterious horse.

7) *Painted Ponies* stand as monuments that honor the pride, courage, spirituality and culture of the First Americans… the Native Americans.

8) *Painted Ponies* are works of art that capture the imagination in a way that brings out the artist in everyone.

9) When you look at *Painted Ponies* they make you feel happy for no apparent reason… like the feeling you get when you are pleasantly surprised.

10) *Painted Ponies* can be enjoyed by adults and children equally.

Painted Ponies have become one of those emotionally inspiring collectibles that people bond with on a variety of levels for a variety of reasons. *Painted Ponies* are a collectible that communicates. They communicate visually compelling imagery. They communicate the inspiration of an artist. They communicate a story. *Painted Ponies* are a collectible that connects. Connects people to others special to them. Connects people to important memories. Connects people to feelings they want to hold on to.

In other words, by giving people a means of communicating that connects them to others, in the process enhancing a sense of community, *The Trail of Painted Ponies* are doing what trails have done since the beginning of time... bringing people together.

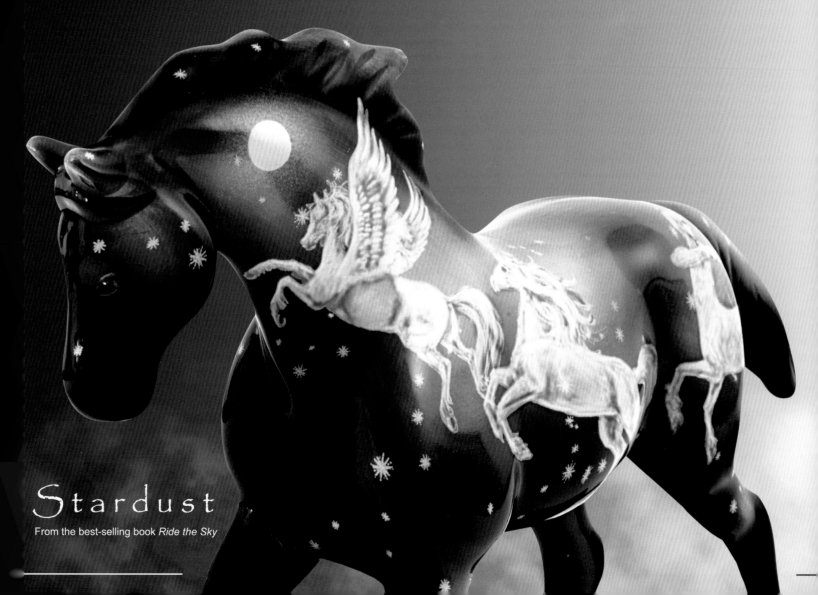

*T*o ride a horse
is to ride the sky.

Stardust

From the best-selling book *Ride the Sky*

The Collector's Guide

FROM FIGURINES TO MERCHANDISE

The Collector's Guide

FROM FIGURINES TO MERCHANDISE

*D*ear Collector,

It has been five years since the first *Trail of Painted Ponies* figurines appeared on the art scene, and we want to thank you, the collector, for making them one of the most popular and memorable collectibles of the New Millennium. We recognize that the world is filled with things to collect, and we want you to know that we are committed to creating a collectible that is appreciated for its beauty, craftsmanship and affordability. We will maintain these high standards. You have our word on it.

Now we invite you to enjoy The Collector's Guide. This is the first, the most comprehensive, and the only authorized guide to *The Trail of Painted Ponies* collectible figurines and merchandise. We are sure you will find it to be an invaluable resource.

In this Guide you will learn the answers to the most commonly asked questions about *The Trail of Painted Ponies* figurines. You will also find a sculpture chart that will help you identify the three distinct positions of *Painted Ponies*, a description of how these magnificent miniature artworks are created, and a list of many of the Native American symbols painted on *The Trail's Native Ponies*, along with their meaning.

*M*aking up the heart of this guide is a Story Tag Directory that features detailed information about every figurine crafted to date, including the most recent release. Along with an image of each figurine you will find a picture of the original *Painted Pony*, its Story Tag, information related to Retired *Ponies*, the awards it has received, and a list of companion merchandise. A section devoted to each of the Special Editions comes next, which will bring you to a set of pages dedicated to our *Paint Your Own Pony Kits* and the various ways they have kindled creative spirits across America!

The Trail of Painted Ponies Collector's Guide would not be complete if it did not include a section dedicated to other collectibles and merchandise spawned by *Painted Ponies* imagery. The Collectibles & More section will take you on a tour, beginning with our newest collectible, gorgeous Jeweled Gift Boxes! Along with original art and collectibles, *The Trail of Painted Ponies* has developed a national reputation for publishing award-winning books, all of which are showcased in this Collector's Guide.

Finally, we tell you more about a secret called "Treasures form the Vault," where serious collectors may find rare and hard-to-find *Trail of Painted Ponies* collectibles, merchandise, and unique original works of art, available exclusively through the *Official Trail of Painted Ponies Website*.

We told you this was comprehensive!

Happy Reading, Happy Collecting, and Happy Trails!

Prairie Horizon
Bob Coonts

Facts About Figurines

*I*n this section of the Collectors Guide you will find the answers to the questions most commonly asked by *Painted Ponies* collectors. Other questions will be answered in the pages that follow.

How many original *Painted Ponies* have been created?
There are 150 life-size *Painted Ponies*, more than 100 Maquettes and 40 Masterworks that have been created to date.

How many *Painted Ponies* submissions have you received and approved?
The Trail has received thousands of submissions from competitions, contests, *Paint Your Own Pony Kits* and general submissions. All of these designs are archived in *The Trail of Painted Ponies* library and reviewed for consideration on a regular basis.

How many figurines have been crafted to date?
The total number of *Painted Ponies* figurines created through 2008 are 138.
This includes: 108 general release Ponies; 20 Holiday Ponies; 6 Exclusive *Painted Ponies*; and 4 Ponies in the Four Seasons Collection.

How many releases have there been?
There have been 12 releases - one release every six months since 2003.

How many of the figurines are resin, and how many ceramic?
There are 38 ceramic figurines, and 100 resin figurines.

How many different positions do the *Painted Ponies* come in?
They are crafted in three positions: Standing, Running and Walking.

How many *Painted Ponies* have been crafted in each position?
Standing: 63, Running: 48, and Walking: 27.

What are the factors that determine the value of a *Painted Ponies* figurines on the secondary market?
The wonder and delight of collecting *Painted Ponies* is enhanced by the fact that they have become a collectible that can significantly increases in value. While at this time it's impossible to post a reliable price guide, and we are reluctant to encourage people to speculate in *Painted Ponies* for investment purposes, the following factors come into play when it comes to determining the value of a *Painted Ponies* figurine: Its artistic beauty. Its popularity. Its current condition. Its scarcity. Whether it is retired. Its edition number (lower edition numbers are prized by serious collectors). Whether it is autographed by the artist. If it is part of the Official Autographed Edition. The condition of the box it comes in. How much it is desired by other collectors.

*H*ow do you continue to come up with fresh *Painted Ponies* designs?
We receive designs daily from artists who have downloaded the horse form from our website and created an original *Painted Pony* concept. Some artists prefer to work directly on a Pony from the *Paint Your Own Pony Kit*, and then submit a digital photograph for our consideration. Regularly we hold national competitions on an announced theme, and sometimes we will issue a call for designs exclusively to those artists who have signed up for our artist data base. Whether the artist is well-known or unknown, we always welcome new designs.

How do you decide which *Ponies* will be released as figurines?
A variety of factors are taken into consideration, including originality and quality, whether the design has striking visual appeal, and whether it is different from anything we've created before. Some designs lend themselves naturally to reproduction, and some are too complex to be seriously considered for miniaturization.

How do you decide which *Painted Ponies* figurines will be cast in resin and which in ceramic?
The decision is based solely on the complexity of the design. Designs with attachments that will require the sculpting of a new mold before production, will be cast in resin. Designs that can be most effectively reproduced through the application of decals or painting will be crafted in ceramic.

Are *Painted Ponies* mass-produced?
The Trail of Painted Ponies figurines are hand-crafted by skilled artisans. The creation process of every *Painted Pony* requires the attention of these extraordinary craftsmen. Talented sculptors are involved in the initial stage of creating resin *Ponies*, and specialists adept at applying decals or hand-painting, create the ceramic *Ponies*. Both resin and ceramic *Painted Ponies* are the result of extensive, individual craftsmanship, which is why there are variations among the *Ponies*. No two *Painted Ponies* are exactly alike. There are even collectors who buy multiple figurines to enjoy the variations that naturally occur as a result of this unique process. (See: Making Magic on page 56)

Would you explain the numbering system on the *Painted Ponies*?
Each *Pony* is sequentially numbered on the bottom of the base according to the order in which it is cast. We release eight new *Painted Ponies* every six months (on June 1 and December 1). There are 10,000 Ponies in each edition, and when that number of *Ponies* have been cast, the edition number changes (1E, First Edition, 2E, Second Edition, etc.)

What are Pre-E's?
The first 3600 castings of the resin *Ponies* in the very first release did not have an edition number written on the bottom (*War Pony, Caballio Brillante, Motorcycle Mustang, Karuna, Boot Scootin' Horsey, and Fireman Pony*). This created an anomaly in the world of collectibles and these figurines are prized by collectors.

Are the *Painted Ponies* limited editions?
Each figurine starts out as an open edition, but every six months (July 1 and January 1) we retire six *Painted Ponies*. This means no more will be produced, in effect making that particular *Painted Pony* part of a limited edition.

Which *Painted Ponies* have been retired? Which *Painted Ponies* are available in merchandise other than figurines?
The answer to these and other questions can be found in the Story Tag Directory that follows.

If you have additional questions, please email: info@trailofpaintedponies.com or visit: www.trailofpaintedponies.com.

Original Painted Ponies Sculptures

	Life-size	**Masterwork**	**Maquette**
	5' tall x 7' long Cast in poly-resin 150 Originals 2001-Current	24" tall x 24" long Cast in bonded marble 40 Originals 2006-Current	12" tall x 12" long Cast in resin More than 100 Originals 2001-2006

STANDING

RUNNING

WALKING

Figurines & Ornaments

9" Figurine	6" to 7" Figurines	Ornaments
9" tall Cast in resin 2004-Current	6" to 7" tall Cast in ceramic and resin 2003-Current	2.5" tall Cast in resin 2004-Current

STANDING

RUNNING

WALKING

Making Magic

When we say that *The Trail of Painted Ponies* figurines are miniature works of art, we mean more than they are inspired by original artworks which they are. We mean that we take such great care in assuring that the figurines are artfully crafted in a way that honors the spirit and is true to the detail of the original *Painted Ponies*, that they are works of art unto themselves. How this is accomplished is a story of magic....

Once we decide that we would like to reproduce an original *Painted Pony* as a figurine, we take detailed photographs from all angles. These photographs are then sent to our collectible manufacturer in China. Not all collectible manufacturers are equal in their abilities, and we work with the very best in the collectible business. They have successfully attracted talented artisans to work for them.

Painted Ponies figurines are cast in one of two materials. If the design on the original *Pony* can be best captured photographically, high resolution decals will be applied to a ceramic figurine. The detailed process of applying decals takes great skill and the artisans who work in this field are specialists. If, on the other hand, there are attachments to the original design or a judgement is made to give the figurine dimensionality, then the figurine will be cast in resin, which requires the involvement of sculptors. These talented artisans understand how important it is to meet the high standards expected of them, and they truly enjoy creating *Painted Ponies*. They take great pride in their work.

Drawing on photographs and sculpting in clay, the sculptors work in painstaking fashion to get every detail on each *Pony* right. Because they are working from photographs and in miniature, they want to make sure that the *Ponies* they sculpt meticulously represent the original. When they feel they have a finished replica, they send back detailed pictures of the *Ponies* they have sculpted in clay.

At this stage in the process we involve the artist who created the original *Pony*. We forward the photos of the clays, ask for comments, and respect their feedback. Often this approval process involves multiple exchanges, which we consider critically important because we want the artist to have a hand in the entire process.

Once we are comfortable with the sculpting of the miniature, a mold is created and the *Pony* is cast in a solid resin material. It is then forwarded to the Art Department, which is staffed with the best miniaturist painters in the business. They have to be the best because what they produce will be the model that all future castings refer to. The approval process for the painted prototype generally follows the same pattern as with the sculpting. Photos are sent to us, we present them to the artist, and the artist lets us know if there are any changes to be made.

Usually a team of painters is assigned to a particular *Pony*, and each *Pony* has Quality Control craftsmen at different points in the process, who oversee each *Pony* as it comes through to assure it is as close to the approved sample as possible. Invariably there will be individual variations, but overall the ability of these talented artisans to create a figurine that can accurately be described as an authentic replica of the original is extraordinary. (Please note, all paints used in the creation of *Painted Ponies* figurines are lead-free.)

When you think about all the attention, all the care that goes into creating each *Painted Pony* figurine, it's little wonder that these figurines have become one of the most popular collectibles in America, indeed in the world. They really are more than figurines. They are truly miniature works of art!

1.

In response to our national call for submissions to "The Native Art of Horse Painting" competition, we received a submission from a Minnesota artist, that had power and was memorable. The title was "Sundancer" and it was accompanied by the story of the annual Sun Dance, begun in the late 19th Century, believed to bring back the buffalo.

Sundancer

2.

In the winter of 2007, recalling the design, we contacted Joyce Kennedy and invited her to refine and simplify her drawing of "Sundancer" in preparation for its translation into a figurine. She created an original drawing from all angles.

3.

A clay sample of "Sundancer" was created and sent to the artist for her comments. Photos of all figurines at this stage are sent to the artists for review, in order to assure their faithfulness to the original design.

4.

The final "Sundancer" figurine was released Summer 2008.

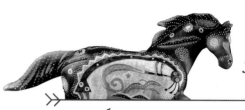

Native American Symbols

The Native American tradition of painting horses before great hunts or battles, has a long and distinguished history in America. These horses were so revered by many Native tribes that they were "honored" or painted with tribal symbols, which were intended to give them special powers and protection.

The meaning of some of these symbols varied from tribe to tribe. However, common symbols were used to decorate horses for ceremony or war. Many of these are featured in this Symbols Directory:

Arrow: Symbolizing power and direction with force and movement. *Indian Summer, Medicine Horse, Reunion of the Family of Man, Prairie Horizon, Wie-Tou*

Bear: Protector with strength and leadership. In Creation Stories, the bear is referenced as the "first helper." Many times, an arrow is depicted on the bear, indicating the "heartline" or path to the heart. *Many Tribes, Native Jewel Pony, Wie-Tou*

Bear Paw: Signifying strength of leadership and authority. *Indian Summer, Spirits of the Northwest, Sacred Reflections of Time, Wie-Tou*

Bold Patterns: Waves and spirals represent water and cycles of life that include renewal and springtime. Combinations of many patterns created by the artists indicate an understanding of these complex symbols. *Anasazi Spirit Horse, Spirit War Pony, Many Tribes, Wie-Tou*

Buffalo: Sacred animal that represents wisdom, experience and abundance. *War Pony, Sounds of Thunder, Kindred Spirits, Native Jewel Pony, Wie-Tou*

Buffalo Skull: A reminder of this sacred animal that has vanished. *War Pony, Sacred Reflections of Time, Sundancer, Wie-Tou*

Circle Around the Eye: Painted on ponies to give them keen eyesight for hunting or battle. *Trail of Honor, Spirit War Pony, Medicine Horse, Reunion of the Family of Man, Runs the Bitterroot, Woodland Hunter, Horse With No Name, Kindred Spirits, Prairie Horizon*

Corn: A symbol of renewal life and the essential crop that sustains life. *Indian Summer, Reunion of the Family of Man, Grandfather's Journey*

Coup Marks: Painted "stripes" indicating the number of enemies killed in battle. *Trail of Honor, War Pony, Medicine Horse, Reunion of the Family of Man, Woodland Hunter, Horse With No Name, Sounds of Thunder, Prairie Horizon*

Coyote: Trickster who is an excellent hunter. *Wie-Tou, Sacred Reflections of Time*

Cross: Where two paths come together or cross. *Ghost Horse, War Pony, Spirits of the Northwest, Cheyenne Painted Rawhide, Indian Summer, Grandfather's Journey*

Dragonfly: Representing water, springtime and renewal. Also thought to be a special messenger. *Indian Summer, War Pony, Thunderbird Suite*

The Eagle: Master of the skies that carries prayers upward to the Creator. The Eagle possesses courage and wisdom and is a great protector. Often confused with the "Thunderbird". *Ghost Horse, Wie-Tou*

Eagle Feathers: Representing prayers or high honor, connecting the user with the Creator. Feathers may be depicted plain or decorated. *Sundancer, Cheyenne Painted Rawhide, Fancy Dancer, Dream Warriors, Horse With No Name, Copper Enchantment, Native Jewel Pony, Runs the Bitterroot, Trail of Honor, Crazy Horse, Indian Summer, Grandfather's Journey, Sounds of Thunder, Medicine Horse, High Desert Horse Feathers, Reunion of the Family of Man, Woodland Hunter, Kachina Pony, The Magician, War Pony, Sacred Reflections of Time, Wie-Tou*

Hail Stones: Hail Stones provide superior strength and speed to the horse and rider. *Trail of Honor, Crazy Horse, Dreamwalker, War Pony, Spirit War Pony, Reunion of the Family of Man, Woodland Hunter, The Magician, Horse With No Name, Spirits of the Northwest, Sounds of Thunder*

Handprint: Left handprint on right hip of horse represents success and safe return from battle. In the Apache and Comanche tribes, a handprint on the right shoulder signifies the enemies defeat and death. *Sundancer, Thunderbird Suite, Reunion of the Family of Man, Woodland Hunter, Trail of Honor, Unity, War Pony, Ghost Horse, Blue Medicine, Sounds of Thunder, Copper Enchantment, Spirit War Pony, Tewa Horse, Dances with Hooves, Medicine Horse, Horse With No Name, Wie-Tou*

Horse or Hoof Prints: Depicting a journey or travels. *Sundancer, The Magician, Horse With No Name, Sounds of Thunder, Prairie Horizon, Wie-Tou*

Kokopelli: One of the most popular and recognizable Native symbols, this flute-playing character represents fertility and enchants young maidens with his music. The Kokopelli is considered an ambassador to the great Southwest. *Many Tribes, Kokopelli Pony, Wie-Tou*

Medicine Wheel & The Four Directions: American Indian Spirituality is symbolized by this circle. There are Four Cardinal Directions and the Four Sacred Colors within the Circle of Life. Black for the west, Red for the north, Yellow for the east, White for the south. *Dreamwalker, High Desert Horse Feathers, Guardian Spirit, Fancy Dancer, Sundancer, Runs the Bitterroot, Sacred Reflections of Time*

Morning Star & Moon: The brightest star on the dawn's horizon representing guidance and direction. The Ghost Dance Religion recognizes this star as a symbol of renewal, tradition and remembrance of fallen warriors. *Kokopelli Pony, Grandfather's Journey, Native Jewel Pony, Caballito, Ghost Horse, War Pony, Spirit War Pony, Reunion of the Family of Man, Spirits of the Northwest, Guardian Spirit, Copper Enchantment, Runs the Bitterroot, Wie-Tou*

Sun Kachina Face: Giver of life, warmth, growth, and all that is good. This style of sun features the face of a Kachina. Similar styles are seen throughout the Southwestern Indian cultures and may depict "rays" signifying the four directions. *Indian Summer, Kachina Pony, Wie-Tou*

Sun of Happiness: Essential giver of life and all that is good. *Horse With No Name, Spirit War Pony, Guardian Spirit, Copper Enchantment, Sounds of Thunder, Prairie Horizon, Navajo Black Beauty, Unity, Indian Summer, Wie-Tou*

Unending Circle: Indicating there is no beginning and no end. *Copper Enchantment, Thunderbird Suite, Dances with Hooves, Prairie Horizon, Wie-Tou*

Thunderbird: Sacred symbol of unlimited happiness. *Ghost Horse, Thunderbird Suite, Sacred Reflections of Time*

Thundercloud: This is an important symbol of change, renewal and good to come. *Dances with Hooves, Grandfather's Journey, Indian Summer*

Thunder Stripes, Lightning or Sky Snake: These bold, jagged lines represent strength, power and storms of change. The feathered sky snake can bring a change in the seasons. All three of these symbols are associated with thunderstorms, lightning and sudden violent changes. *Trail of Honor, War Pony, Medicine Horse, Reunion of the Family of Man, Grandfather's Journey, Woodland Hunter, Horse With No Name, Copper Enchantment, Sounds of Thunder, Wie-Tou*

Every Pony Tells a Story

There is a storytelling tradition to American art that is captured in the phrase: Every picture tells a story. There is a narrative tradition to *Painted Ponies* as well. The artist's inspiration and the meaning behind each *Painted Pony* can be found on the Story Tag that accompanies each figurine.

The *Painted Ponies* speak to everyone differently, and *The Trail* often holds short story contests on its website, inviting collectors to write stories about their favorite *Painted Ponies*. One winning entry, featured below, proved the point: whether a brush is brandished or a pen, the pleasure to be found in the creativity with which artists and writers express themselves is the same.

"I was that horse-crazy little girl - lying in the grass, reading my horsey books. I was that little girl who would rather muck a stall than clean her room - just to be close to horses. Flicka. The Black Stallion. All the Chincoteague Ponies. Black Beauty. Man O' War. Secretariat. Seabiscuit. These historical and fictious horses - plus herds more - galloped through my every dream. From Bucephalus and Pegasus, to 'The Horse Whisperer' and Funny Cide, horses and horse people have been revered, awed and memorialized by the written word. The magical, noble, awe-inspiring horse led me to my love of literature, and I will pass my love of reading on to my children and eventually my grandchildren. To this day I have a voracious appetite for all things equine. If you're ever out my way, look for me. I'll be the horse crazy woman - lying in the grass, reading my horsey books to my son, while my real, live, majestic steeds gallop through my pastures. I can tell you all about horse dreams - and how they really can come true."

Heather Cooper

"My First Painted Pony" Stories

Do you remember your first *Painted Pony*? For a lot of people it was as unforgettable an experience as the first real horse they ever owned. Or rode. Or dreamed about. And so we created a "My First *Pony*" section on our official website, and invited collectors to share their stories...

"I am 7 years old and every time I go to sleep my mom prays with me and since I have received my latest Pony the "Heavenly Pony" I feel even more safe because I know he's from where God comes from."

Sara, Texas

"My husband and I were browsing around the gift shop of a local casino a couple of years ago, and we happened upon a display case of some amazing figurines. He called me over and exclaimed, 'Look at these horses!' We walked away with 'Fetish Pony,' 'Medicine Horse' and 'Woodland Hunter' and I was hooked from that point on."

Sheryl, Oregon

My first Painted Pony was "Rodeo Dreams." He is so beautiful! I live in the U.K and every time I go to the U.S.A. I purchase another Pony to remind me of my trip and where we went. We have been to Florida, Nevada, California and Arizona up to now, so I have 4 Painted Ponies. Thanks for a lovely keepsake of my trips."

Ruth, United Kingdom

Dream Horse
Janee Hughes

Rodeo Dreams
Jim Knauf

Welcome to the Story Tag Directory

The Trail of Painted Ponies respects fine art traditions in many ways. As bronze and porcelain sculptures are often mounted on wood or marble bases, all of the *Painted Ponies* figurines are attached to a base. Just as each fine art sculpture is numbered according to the order in which it is cast, *Painted Ponies* figurines are individually and sequentially numbered on the bottom of their bases according to their casting order. Sculpture is usually cast in limited editions, and while *Painted Ponies* begin as open editions, on a regular basis we "retire" *Ponies*, in effect creating limited editions.

In the comprehensive Story Tag Directory that follows, you will find information about every figurine that has been crafted to date, along with details regarding Retired *Painted Ponies*, awards and companion merchandise. The Directory begins with the newest releases, listed in alphabetical order. You can dowload your own Collectors Checklist from our website at: www.trailofpaintedponies.com

Dreamwalker
Ben Wright

Stagecoach Pony
Johanna Enriquez

Serenity
La Marr

Silverado
Karlynn Keyes

Bunkhouse Bronco

The original bunkhouse was a rough, simple building, often fashioned from the wood boards torn off old barns that provided sleeping quarters for ranch hands. Horse tack, wagon wheels and cow skulls were frequently tacked to weathered planks on the outside, while western hats and ropes hung on the inside walls. Adding cozy ambience, the whole place would smell of coffee brewing in an enamel pot on a wood burning stove. Working these classic, cowboy touches into a fabulous *Painted Pony* design, this gifted Oregon artist has created an old-timey yet timeless tribute to our Western heritage.

Finalist:
America the Beautiful Competition

Artist: Lynn Bean
Item: #12275
Walking Resin

Available As: Ⓐ Official Autographed Edition

7" Figurine

Kachina Pony

Kachinas are stylized religious icons, meticulously carved from cottonwood roots and painted to represent figures from Hopi mythology. They often wear masks of animals, plants, stars, warriors and clowns. They are the focus of ceremonies and rituals in which they relay the wishes of the Hopi people to the spirits – for more rain, a plentiful harvest, and good health. In an effort to create a *Painted Pony* with mystical powers of its own, this colorist from Idaho has adorned her *Pony* with the designs and symbols of traditional kachina masks, including, on the left side, the "Sun Kachina" mask, and on the right, the "Messenger of the Gods" mask.

Artist: Maria Ryan
Item: #12279
Running Resin
Native Pony

Available As: Ⓐ Official Autographed Edition

7" Figurine

For Spacious Skies

"Some of the most famous memorials, monuments and landmarks in our country inspired my *Pony*," says the artist, a full-time graphic designer at the University of Illinois. While acknowledging that Mount Rushmore, the Statue of Liberty, the U.S. Capitol, the Washington Monument, the Lincoln Memorial, and the Iwo Jima Memorial can only be appreciated when experienced in person, she wanted her *Pony* to be a kind of road trip across America… on horseback. The original "For Spacious Skies" was the People's Choice Award Winner of the national "America the Beautiful" competition.

Winner: People's Choice Award
America the Beautiful Competition

Artist: Janet Snyder
Item: #12274
Walking Ceramic

Available As: Ⓐ Official Autographed Edition

7" Figurine

Rolling Thunder

"Rolling Thunder" hearkens back to a time of big skies and fierce storms, of thundering herds of bison large enough to shake the earth beyond the horizon, and of Plains Indians and their spirited, sure-footed, courageous horses trained to carry bow-bearing braves through the stampeding confusion of a bison hunt. Only an artist who has called Oklahoma home her entire life, who has seen with her own eyes the way darkening skies can be splintered with lightning bolts that seem to outline a rumbling "sky herd" of buffalo, could have created this masterful homage to the "buffalo ponies."

Finalist:
Native Art of Horse Painting Competition

Artist: Aloma Wolfington
Item: #12277
Walking Resin
Native Pony

Available As: Ⓐ Official Autographed Edition

7" Figurine

Runs the Bitterroot

The Native Americans' admiration for the horse took many forms. A favored horse dressed for ceremony or war would often be adorned with striking regalia, as well as painted. The beauty and mystery of the Indian horse mask as the emblem of a warrior Pony is captured with great power by an Oklahoma historian/artist in this masterful tribute to Chief Joseph. The legendary leader of the Nez Perce, who are credited with the successful breeding of the Appaloosa, is remembered for his principled resistance to the forced removal of the Nez Perce from their Idaho homelands. Chief Joseph's surrender speech, in which he said "From where the sun now stands, I will fight no more forever," immortalized him in American history and popular culture.
Finalist:
Native Art of Horse Painting Competition

Artist: Kevin Kilhoffer
Item: #12280
Walking Resin
Native Pony

Available As: Ⓐ Official Autographed Edition

7" Figurine

Sundancer

The Sun Dance was the most spectacular and important religious ceremony of the Plains Indians of the 19th century. It was designed to bring renewal – the spiritual rebirth of its participants, harmony between all living beings, and the return of the all-important buffalo. Incorporating many of the sacred materials and symbolic elements of the Sun Dance ceremony into her design – a sage noseband, pictograph horses traveling from each of the four sacred directions, a white buffalo skull, a war bonnet sun graphic – this Minnesota graphics artist has created a *Pony* that represents the essence of the Sun Dance: renewal and balance, and the reaffirmation of relationships between people and nature.

Artist: Joyce Kennedy
Item: #12278
Walking Resin
Native Pony

Available As: Ⓐ Official Autographed Edition

7" Figurine

Stagecoach Pony

Relive the days of overland stagecoach travel in the Old West with a *Painted Pony* that captures a dramatic and symbolic moment in frontier history! Throughout most of the 1800s, stagecoaches were a primary means of transportation across the American West. They hauled passengers, mail and freight over vast, treeless plains, jagged mountain passes, scorching deserts, and rivers cursed with quicksand. To capture the iconic character of the stagecoach, this artist – formerly with National Geographic Magazine's Art Division - imagined a horse-drawn stagecoach running from danger – attacking Indians or outlaw robbers – down a dusty trail, silhouetted against a sunset sky.

Artist: Johanna Enriquez
Item: #12273
Running Ceramic

Available As: Ⓐ Official Autographed Edition

7" Figurine

Wounded Knee

On the frozen banks of Wounded Knee Creek, Lakota Chief Big Foot and his followers huddled together, hungry and exhausted. Driven off their lands, they surrendered and were surrounded by the U.S. 7th Calvary that had been ordered to peacefully escort them to a reservation. There was tension in the air. Troops feared the Sioux and the powerful Ghost Dances that spread through the Dakotas as the Indians frantically danced and prayed for the return of their way of life. A single shot rang out from a Calvary gun and chaos erupted. When the smoke cleared, peaceful Chief Big Foot and all of the Lakota lay dead in the snow. As the sun set on South Dakota, a single Native pony wandered the frozen plains in search of his beloved people that would dance no more.
Artist Choice Award:
Kentucky Horse Park Exhibition

Artist: Vickie Knepper
Item: #12276
Running Resin
Native Pony

Available As: Ⓐ Official Autographed Edition

7" Figurine

Crazy Horse

History books describe Crazy Horse as a respected war leader who fought against the U.S. government in an effort to preserve the traditions and values of the Lakota way of life. He was that and much more. As a young man he had a vivid dream of a horseback rider, with lightning zig-zagging down his cheek and a turquoise earring in one ear, who looked up to see a red-backed hawk fly overhead. When he related the dream to his medicine man father, Crazy Horse was told he would achieve future greatness in battle. A lifetime of victories on the battlefield followed, culminating with his triumph over George Armstrong Custer at the Little Bighorn. No photographs of Crazy Horse exist, but with this *Pony* CJ Wells, a Native "artist warrior" herself, has given him a high-voltage interpretation.

Artist: CJ Wells
Item: #12264
Standing Resin
Native Pony

Available As: (A) Official Autographed Edition

6" Figurine

Indian Summer

An agricultural people, the Hopi have sustained themselves for millennia in the northern Arizona desert without the benefit of rivers or streams. The Hopi Way is to work hard, pray, sing, take part in ceremonies, and create images they believe will summon help from spirit beings. This Hopi artist has incorporated a variety of traditional Hopi symbols into his design, all of which revolve around rain and moisture, and a successful harvest. Butterfly Maidens are believed to help pollinate crops. Nothing could grow without the sun. Dragonflies are signs of a natural spring.

Artist: Buddy Tubinaghtewa (Hopi)
Item: #12266
Running Resin
Native Pony

Available As: (A) Official Autographed Edition

7" Figurine

Dreamwalker

Drawing on his Cherokee heritage, this Arizona artist, whose large, spiritually powerful portraits of Native American warriors are coveted by museums, has created a visual interpretation of the traditional tale of the "Dreamwalker." It is a story about a medicine man who is told in a vision that "the discovery of power will come through the ways of animals." Shortly thereafter he sets out on a trek across the Great Plains, to the east, where illumination lives. He carries a pipe with him. He has many encounters. He draws on the powers of a medicine wheel. Near the end of his journey he is greeted by a white stallion who tells him the secret of "true power" is compassion, caring and sharing one's gift with others.

Finalist:
Native Art of Horse Painting Competition

Artist: Ben Wright (Cherokee)
Item: #12263
Walking Resin
Native Pony

Available As: (A) Official Autographed Edition

7" Figurine

Prairie Horizon

This fine artist from Colorado has a long fascination with the history and lore of the Nez Perce Indians - expert horsemen with a sophisticated knowledge of breeding who are credited with developing the Appaloosa. Using a distinctive artistic style that combines bold colors with geometric shapes, circles, triangles and arrows that connect his design to the title – a horizon line encircles the horse, grass and trees, canyons and rivers are rendered in an abstract way - he breathes new life and excitement into his stylized interpretation of a breed of horse known for its unique color and variety of spots.

Finalist:
Native Art of Horse Painting Competition

Artist: Bob Coonts
Item: #12261
Walking Ceramic
Native Pony

Available As: (A) Official Autographed Edition

7" Figurine

Serenity

It's said that serenity is not freedom from the storm, but peace amid the storm. With that in mind, this California artist set out to decorate her *Pony* with designs that put the heart at ease. She was inspired by such classically popular patterns as Blue Willow, a design that has graced the world's finest dinnerware. (Who can resist the charming imagery of the star-crossed lovers who were turned into immortal lace birds?) And Coventry Blue, a delicate embroidery found on white linen and bed coverings that originated in 16th Century England and evokes pastoral strolls down shady lanes past white cottages and ponds dappled with lilies.

Artist: La Marr
Item: #12260
Running Ceramic

Available As: Ⓐ Official Autographed Edition

7" Figurine

Twilight Hunters

It's a crisp, icy evening and there's a scent in the wind. The cold silence is split by a piercing chorus of howls, followed by the shuffle of padded feet crunching through the snow. The pack picks up the pace. Their breath makes small clouds. The twilight hunters are prowling for prey in the last light of day…. With this scene in her mind, this New Mexico western and wildlife painter has created a contemporary tribute to the wild wolves of the west.

Artist: Lori Musil
Item: #12262
Running Resin

Available As: Ⓐ Official Autographed Edition

7" Figurine

Trail of Honor

At this time in our history, it is important to acknowledge all the men and women who have served, and are serving in our armed forces, including those of Native American ancestry. The inspiration for this Pony came to a Virginia-based artist while attending a Powwow, when she saw an American flag and an Eagle staff carried proudly by two Native American veterans of foreign wars. She imagined a *Painted Pony* that symbolically connected those warriors who courageously fought against the United States government, with those who proudly fought to protect America. It would be a white *Pony* painted with traditional Plains Indian symbols, standing between Old Glory and an Eagle Staff, with a royal blue coverlet draped over the horse's back on which were sewn patches from each of the United States Armed Forces: the Army, Marines, Navy, Air Force and Coast Guard.

Artist: Devon Archer
Item: #12267
Walking Resin
Native Pony

Available As: Ⓐ Official Autographed Edition

7" Figurine

Wish Upon a Star

Although no unicorn sightings have been reported in centuries, this mysteriously beautiful creature is alive and well in legend and myth, and in our hearts and minds. Believed to be a fabulous hybrid with the body of a white horse, the cloven hooves of a goat, a lion's tail, and a slender, golden spiral horn on its forehead, the unicorn is an animal of good omen and magical qualities. It is reported to appear to true believers when the time is right. The perfect gift for unicorn lovers, "Wish Upon a Star" was created by the multi-talented artist who sculpted all the original *Painted Pony* horse forms.

Artist: Star Liana York
Item: #12265
Running Resin

Available As: Ⓐ Official Autographed Edition

7" Figurine

Boot Camp

A cowboy's best friends are his horse and saddle, a rope, a hat and a comfortable pair of boots. But boy howdy, when it comes to *Painted Ponies* you can forget the plain, clunky, brown and black working cowboy boot. Banishing the traditional "high heels of the range" from her imagination, Idaho wildlife artist Maria Ryan created a colorful tribute to the cowboy boot mystique when she bedecked and bedazzled her *Pony* with an outrageous collection of western fashion footwear and let him kick up his heels.

Artist: Maria Ryan
Item: #12250
Running Resin

Available As: (A) Official Autographed Edition

7" Figurine
Ornament

Dynasty Pony

China is a land of myths and mysteries shrouded in the mists of history. Throughout the course of Chinese history, one animal has exerted a tremendous influence over its development - the horse. Drawing on Imperial artifacts and records dating back to the Qing Dynasty (when the golden dragon symbolized the Emperor), Jeffrey Chan, a former art director in the movie industry in Hong Kong who now works in giftware design, created a glorious "warrior pony" that has the richly detailed feel and look of an archaeological art treasure.

Artist: Jeffrey Chan
Item: #12251
Running Resin

Available As:

7" Figurine

Ceremonial Pony

Cathy Smith is a historian and scholar of the American West. She is also an authentic costumer who has worked on such films as "Dances with Wolves" and "All the Pretty Horses." Her original *Pony* was adorned with a Crow woman's horse trappings outfit, circa 1870's. The keyhole-shaped ornament on the forehead was a classic Crow design, the beaded rosette surrounded with horsehair tassels and wrapped in dyed cotton string. Made to carry a short buffalo lance or captured cavalry sword, the case was fashioned out of buffalo rawhide painted with natural earth pigments. Outfits similar to this are still paraded today at the Crow Fair in Crow Agency, Montana.

Artist: Cathy Smith
Item: #12255
Standing Resin
Native Pony

Available As: (A) Official Autographed Edition

6" Figurine

Navajo Black Beauty

As well as for their famous rugs, Navajo weavers are known for their beautiful, pictorial, basket weavings. Many illustrate themes and tell stories that preserve Navajo history. Barbara Duzan, an Arizona artist who has distinguished herself internationally with her one-of-a-kind, beaded animals, wanted to pay special tribute to this unique tribal tradition by beading a *Pony* that carried "Man Placing the Stars," a Navajo creation myth, on one side of her *Pony*, and "Sun's Journey through the Sky" on the other. Each design is rendered in the Navajo basket weaver's style.

Finalist:
Native Art of Horse Painting Competition

Artist: Barbara Duzan
Item: #12254
Walking Resin
Native Pony

Available As: (A) Official Autographed Edition

7" Figurine

Northern Lights

Horses are familiar to all of us, but many of the world's most beautiful animals live in remote precincts on the planet and are far less familiar. The award-winning painter and book illustrator, Janee Hughes, created this spectacular tribute to some of the creatures that are at home in the vast distances of the arctic. On one side you will find the animals that spend most of their lives in the forests and mountains – the Arctic Wolf, the caribou – and on the other are animals that live mostly in the sea or on sea ice – the walrus, polar bear, humpback whale. Above them all are the breathtaking, shifting, shimmering, Northern Lights.

Artist: Janee Hughes
Item: #12249
Walking Ceramic

Available As: (A) Official Autographed Edition

7" Figurine
Puzzle

Stardust

"From stardust we have come, and to stardust we shall return," writes Janee Hughes, an artist and writer from the Pacific Northwest as gifted with a pen as with a brush. "Between times, many have gazed in wonder at the night sky and thought they've seen figures in the arrangement of stars and galaxies. In centuries past, fertile imaginations have even gone so far as to conjure gods and heroes and tell their stories in terms of myths. Many involve the horse, our respected companion on earth, our friend in the heavens...."

Artist: Janee Hughes
Item: #12248
Running Ceramic

Available As: (A) Official Autographed Edition

7" Figurine
Jeweled Gift Box

Sacred Reflections of Time

In her artistic creations, this Arkansas artist of Cherokee descent (her Indian name is Silver Fox) strives to capture the Native American's respect for the sacredness and beauty of Mother Earth, the colorful legends handed down from generation to generation, and the love and close bond that was shared with the horse. "'Sacred Reflections' is my Spirit Horse and Peace Pony. She carries an Eagle on her shield, a buffalo on her pipe and bag, a coyote on her quiver and a bear paw on the smaller drum. These are the guardians of the four major directions, and they are also great teachers."

Artist: Joani Jiannine
Item: #12253
Running Resin
Native Pony

Available As: (A) Official Autographed Edition

7" Figurine
Ornament

Wie-Tou

Growing up on a Colorado horse ranch across the valley from her Cherokee grandfather, this artist was immersed at an early age in both Indian art and culture and the riding life. Painting horses and Indian symbols on leather helped pay for her college tuition. It also inspired her to create a *Pony* whose power lies in the graphically creative arrangement of assorted spiritual symbols. "I wanted to include the Spirits that guide and protect us, and every one I've painted has 'good medicine.'"

Finalist:
Native Art of Horse Painting Competition

Artist: Barbara Janowitz
Item: #12252
Walking Resin
Native Pony

Available As: (A) Official Autographed Edition

7" Figurine

Retired: July 2008
Retirement #2E/8617

Bedazzled

To ride on a carousel is every child's dream, and most adults find that carousels bring back the joys of childhood. "Bedazzled" embodies all the characteristics of the Coney Island carousel style that reached its peak at the turn of the 20th Century. "Her silver dapple coat, flowing gold mane and tail, and sparkling jewels would bring squeals of delight from any child," says creator J.E. Speight, who studied the various styles of the famous early carousels while serving as the head painter on several restored carousel horses in Salem, Oregon's Riverfront Park.

Artist: J.E. Speight
Item: #12245
Running Resin

Available As: Ⓐ Official Autographed Edition

7" Figurine

Copper Enchantment

The multi-talented Oregon artist Lynn Bean, who also created "Fetish Pony," wanted to adorn an appaloosa horse with traditional Native symbols of power, spirit and strength, rendered in different mediums. Using hand-tooled copper foil, leather, feathers and beads to form lightning bolts on the neck (signifying speed), and a handprint on the hindquarters (signifying ownership), she has given birth to an original vision of beauty and wonder appropriately titled "Copper Enchantment."

Finalist:
Native Art of Horse Painting Competition

Artist: Lynn Bean
Item: #12244
Walking Resin
Native Pony

Available As: Ⓐ Official Autographed Edition

7" Figurine	Ornament
9" Figurine	
Ball Cap	
Clothing	
Jeweled Gift Box	

Cheyenne Painted Rawhide

An appreciation of all earthly and spiritual gifts in the Native American culture and traditions led this gifted Montana artist to create a *Painted Pony* that honored an authentic Native art form not widely known. After thoroughly researching the Cheyenne woman's tradition of painting abstract designs of spiritual significance on dressed, buffalo hides, Liz conceived of a *Painted Pony* design that, in the words of a tribal elder, "is a beauty and has won my heart." The original "Cheyenne Rawhide Pony" was selected as Best of Show by *Southwest Art Magazine* in "The Native Art of Horse Painting Competition."
Finalist:
Native Art of Horse Painting Competition

Artist: Liz Chappie-Zoller
Item: #12242
Walking Resin
Native Pony

Available As: Ⓐ Official Autographed Edition

7" Figurine

Fancy Dancer

The Fancy Dance evolved from the early Plains tribe's war and victory dances. It is an energetic style of dance, usually performed by younger men who spin, twist, and make quick steps and fast turns. Their outfits are traditionally composed of lots of bright colors, metallic beads, sequins and ribbons which create a flashy display. They have two bustles, a head roach and intricately beaded headband... all of which are faithfully and stunningly recreated on a spirited, snorting horse that is caught up in the excitement of the drum beat. This unique creation by a Virginia artist won "The People's Choice Award" in the national competition, "The Native Art of Horse Painting."
Winner: People's Choice Award
Native Art of Horse Painting Competition

Artist: Devon Archer
Item: #12247
Walking Resin
Native Pony

Available As: Ⓐ Official Autographed Edition

7" Figurine
9" Figurine
Lamp

Native Jewel Pony

Adornment – jewelry of silver and turquoise, bead work and ceremonial regalia – is a defining element and recognized hallmark of cultural expression for North American Indians. Maria Ryan - an accomplished artist and designer from Coeur d'Alene, Idaho - has been winning awards and pleasing collectors around the world for decades. Her research into the meanings and symbolism behind the designs used in classic Southwestern jewelry, coupled with a fearless artistic style that leads her to experiment with different materials to achieve special effects in her art, resulted in this stunning tribute to the Native American love of jewelry.

Finalist:
Native Art of Horse Painting Competition
Artist: Maria Ryan
Item: #12243
Walking Resin
Native Pony

Available As: Ⓐ Official Autographed Edition

7" Figurine
Jeweled Gift Box
Ornament

Sounds of Thunder

This *Painted Pony* represents both the male and female lifestyle of the Plains Indian People, as rendered by the acclaimed Cherokee father and daughter artists, Bill and Traci Rabbit. On Side 1, Bill depicts the ultimate warrior – his profile accompanied by symbols that tell the dramatic story of his many victories. On Side 2, Traci depicts the grace, strength and determination of women in Native society – a sun radiating healing beams, her dress signifying her skill at beading and design, a buffalo hunt in the background relating the importance of both the buffalo and the horse to Native Americans.

Finalist:
Native Art of Horse Painting Competition

Artist: Bill and Traci Rabbit (Cherokee)
Item: #12240
Walking Ceramic
Native Pony

Available As: Ⓐ Official Autographed Edition

7" Figurine
Puzzle

Silverado

During the first half of the 20th century, parades and horse shows held in conjunction with rodeos, fiestas and fairs throughout the West fueled a demand for fancy, embroidered saddlery. Elegant, silver-mounted parade saddles, carved with floral and figural motifs, and with matching bridles, martingales and breast collars, were perceived as exquisite works of art. "Silverado," a customized interpretation of this flashy tradition by Karlynn Keyes, Vice-President of *The Trail of Painted Ponies*, is a masterpiece by any definition.

Artist: Karlynn Keyes
Item: #12241
Walking Resin

Available As: Ⓐ Official Autographed Edition

7" Figurine
Ball Cap
Clothing
Ornament

Viva Las Vegas

No other icon epitomizes Las Vegas like the "Show Girl." Known for her incredibly elaborate, baroque but brief costumes; her ability to sing, dance and sashay across a stage in sky-high stilettos, while balancing a feathered headdress atop her head; the "Show Girl" is considered a piece of art or a human sculpture. Although "Show Girl" revues are slowly disappearing on The Strip, the Stockton, California artist who paints under the name LaMarr, wanted to take us on a ride through Las Vegas entertainment history with this dazzling tribute.

Artist: LaMarr
Item: #12246
Walking Resin

Available As: Ⓐ Official Autographed Edition

7" Figurine
Ball Cap
Clothing

Blondes

David DeVary is one of an emerging group of so-called "New West" artists who celebrate the myths of the American West. His oil and gold-leaf paintings boldly colored and dramatically top lit, present contemporary cowboys and cowgirls in the guise of romanticized American icons. Posed like glamorous fashion models on the sides of a beautiful Palomino, their eyes shadowed by a low-tipped cowboy hat, women on this *Pony* intentionally glorify the freedom and self-confidence we associate with "the cowgirl."

Artist: David DeVary
Item: #12227
Standing Ceramic

Available As: Ⓐ Official Autographed Edition

6" Figurine

Dream Warriors

"My best designs come to me when I am quiet," says Colorado artist Ross Lampshire, perhaps best known as a rodeo photographer and potter. "An idea or image enters my mind almost as a whisper… and fast takes on a life of its own." Inspired by written accounts of Sitting Bull's dreams prior to battle, Ross had his own dream one night of Sitting Bull silhouetted against a full moon with clouds parting, as if in search of a vision. Working in a stylized manner, Ross has created a dramatic, powerful and flowing design that honors this famous Sioux Chief.

Finalist:
Native Art of Horse Painting Competition

Artist: Ross Lampshire
Item: #12233
Walking Resin
Native Pony

Available As: Ⓐ Official Autographed Edition

7" Figurine
9" Figurine
Ornament

Dog and Pony Show

If you love dogs, you have come to the right place. Sedona wildlife artist Gene Dieckhoner - whose noteworthy accomplishments include serving as Art Director for Fox Animation Studios- has created a delightful tribute to our "faithful friends." Pure breeds and mixed breeds alike are gathered together on the form of a horse - another companion animal-that itself has been painted to resemble a Doberman Pinscher. For the dog and horse lover, this pony is the next best thing to owning your own!

Artist: Gene Dieckhoner
Item: #12231
Standing Resin

Available As: Ⓐ Official Autographed Edition

6" Figurine
Puzzle

Guardian Spirit

Deer and wolves that speak to man, arrows that carry prayers, serpents that bring rain – are all real in the Huichol Indian belief system. The Huichol live in the Sierra Madre Mountains of central Mexico, and for centuries these spiritual people have been beading decorative items to use as offerings to the gods. Their world is rich in symbolism and imagination and they encode their spiritual knowledge through their art. *The Trail of Painted Ponies* was honored when a Huichol couple agreed to create an original *Pony* intricately beaded with images that represent life and enlightenment.

Artist: The Huichol Indians /
Gregorio & Graciela Medina
Item: #12230
Standing Resin
Native Pony

Available As:

6" Figurine

Retired: July 2008
Retirement #3E/7146

Horse With No Name

A story is told about a riderless Appaloosa, flamboyantly painted with symbols that portray a warrior's bravery during battle, wandering the prairie as if in search of his master. According to this tale, the horse would never let anyone else ride him, though many tried. The lightning bolt on his face, the sun on his shoulder, the circle around his eye, the handprint on his flank, the feathers in his mane and tail marked him as a horse with powerful medicine. And so he was allowed to roam the plains freely… to be eventually memorialized by New Mexico artist Loran Creech.

Artist: Loran Creech
Item: #12229
Standing Resin
Native Pony

Available As: Ⓐ Official Autographed Edition

6" Figurine
Ball Cap
Clothing

Spirits of the Northwest

Animals are important to the northwest native cultures. Using bold colors and designs based on the Haida and Tlingit styles of art, Laurie Holman, who lives and teaches art in Alaska, presents us with various animal totems featured in traditional Alaska stories: the Raven, Grizzly Bear, Salmon, Eagle, and Whale. "I wanted them to cover the entire Pony, like a puzzle, with all the pieces telling the great story of life, death and rebirth.

Finalist:
Native Art of Horse Painting Competition

Artist: Laurie Holman
Item: #12234
Walking Resin
Native Pony

Available As: Ⓐ Official Autographed Edition

7" Figurine

Many Tribes

Pottery is one of the oldest art forms in the Native American culture, and each tribe has a style that is traditionally its own. Today, however, tribal potters borrow or copy designs and techniques from each other. Drawing on the diverse animal and geographic patterns found on many authentic pots, Linda, a Delaware Indian living in Las Vegas, has painted a *Pony* wrapped in the traditional and contemporary ceramic designs of many tribes.

Artist: Linda Hassett
Item: #12228
Running Ceramic
Native Pony

Available As: Ⓐ Official Autographed Edition

7" Figurine

Retired: July 2008
Retirement #3E/7242

Super Charger

In the 15th Century, when knights were defenders of faith, a woman's honor, and just about anything that endowed them with greater glory, so did their "chargers" share in the accolades. In fact, the exalted association of man and horse is precisely what is meant by chivalry - an adaptation of the French word meaning horse-cheval. With this in mind, Rod Barker, President of *The Trail of Painted Ponies*, designed a "Super Charger" fit for the noblest of knights.

Artist: Rod Barker
Item: #12232
Walking Resin

Available As: Ⓐ Official Autographed Edition

7" Figurine
Ball Cap
Clothing

Retired: July 2008
Retirement #4E/0370

Fetish Pony

To Native Americans, a fetish is any object that possesses "spirit power." They believe that when the object is treated with respect, the spirit that resides within can bring its owner good luck, good health and a harmonious life. With this in mind, Oregon painter Lynn Bean created an extraordinary "fetish pony" on which the spirit images of different horses seem to emerge from inside a sandstone carving of a host horse, who wears a "power pack" of feathers, beads, and shells on its back.

Artist: Lynn Bean
Item: #12221
Standing Resin
Native Pony

Available As: Ⓐ Official Autographed Edition

6" Figurine   Stationary
9" Figurine
Ball Cap
Clothing
Ornament

Horsepower to Burn

He came of age in the '50s, when hot rods and drag racing were "cool," when flames and checkered flags were stock images in car magazines. Years later, after three-decades teaching art and coaching basketball and winning an award as the "New Mexico Art Educator of the Year" in 1988, Rich would draw on those times, those memories, when he was encouraged to paint a *Pony* by a NASCAR far.

Artist: Rich Mattson
Item: #12226
Running Ceramic

Available As: Ⓐ Official Autographed Edition

7" Figurine
Mug

Retired: July 2007
Retirement #2E/9001

Gift Horse

In celebration of the way *Painted Ponies* have become the perfect gift for holidays, birthdays and anniversaries, we asked Misty, an artist from Columbus, Ohio who is a member of League of Animal Artists, to create a *Pony* that would be appropriate for every gift-giving occasion. Standing on a beautifully wrapped purple package, dressed with cakes, party hats, streamers, balloons and presents, and wearing a candy-colored halter, "Gift Horse" is a virtual *Painted Pony* Party that is as much fun as it is innovative.

Artist: Misty Lynn Auld
Item: #12225
Standing Ceramic

Available As:

6" Figurine

Retired: January 2007
Retirement #3E/0930

Native People's Pony

"As an artist, I have always had this vision of different cultures around the world coming together sharing their beliefs, customs, blending as one on this small planet we call Mother Earth," says Frank Salcido, a Navajo from the Standing House Clan, living in Portland Oregon. With both sides of his *Pony's* face represented by Aztec and Mayan warriors, adorned with tribal figures from an Australian Aborigine to an African Masai woman, Frank has fulfilled his artistic mission of using positive themes to contemporarily showcase traditional lifestyles.

Artist: Frank Salcido (Navajo)
Item: #12224
Standing Ceramic
Native Pony

Available As: Ⓐ Official Autographed Edition

6" Figurine

Retired: January 2007
Retirement #2E/7201

Silver Lining

In Greek Mythology, Pegasus is regarded as horse of the Muses, and has always been at the service of poets. And so the story is told of a handsome youth who jumped on the back of a horse who unfolded the splendor of a mighty set of wings and soared towards the heavens… where he can still be seen as the star constellation, Pegasus. Santa Fe sculptor and horsewoman Star Liana York created the original, crystal eyed interpretation of the legendary flying steed to benefit a therapeutic horseback riding program.

Artist: Star Liana York
Item: #12219
Running Resin

Available As: Ⓐ Official Autographed Edition

7" Figurine
Ball Cap
Clothing
Stationary

Woodland Hunter

"Woodland Hunter came to me through research and study of the Northern Plains Tribes," says Kevin Kilhoffer, a native of western Oklahoma who studies, draws and paints the American West. "I found records of a Franciscan missionary stationed at a fur trade fort dating back to 1836, and in his notes he described a Teton Sioux warrior who rode into the fort wearing a magnificent war shirt adorned with scalps and wonderful art work decorating his horse." Incorporating markings that tell of deeds, wisdom, wealth and bravery, and outfitting his *Pony* with a shield, weapons, saddle and bags for transporting food, Kevin has created an astounding and historically accurate tribute to that Plains Indian warrior.

Artist: Kevin Kilhoffer
Item: #12220
Standing Resin
Native Pony

Available As: Ⓐ Official Autographed Edition

6" Figurine   Ornament
9" Figurine   Stationary
Ball Cap
Clothing
Lamp

The Magician

In certain Plains Indian Tribes there was a special tribal figure who spoke to and for the horses. He was believed to possess supernatural powers, and was called The "Magician." As rendered by Taos artist Andersen Kee, who was born on the Navajo Reservation and whose mother was a weaver and father a silversmith, the "Magician" is releasing a heard of multi-colored spirit Ponies from the inside of his elks skin robe and then gathering them on the backside.

Artist: Andersen Kee (Navajo)
Item: #12222
Running Resin
Native Pony

Available As: Ⓐ Official Autographed Edition

7" Figurine
Mug

Year of the Horse

Painted in conjunction with the Chinese "Year of the Horse", this western and wildlife artist from Cerrillos, New Mexico created a classic celebration of the different horse breeds of America. From the American Quarter Horse to the Thoroughbred, Appaloosa and American Paint, ten horses move gracefully and majestically across the curves and bulges of the original sculpture, each exhibiting a personality of its own, with a style and flair that is Lori's personal hallmark.

Artist: Lori Musil
Item: #12223
Running Resin

Available As:

7" Figurine   Mug
9" Figurine   Puzzle
Ball Cap   Ornament
Clothing   Stationary
Jeweled Gift Box

American Dream Horse

Asked by a Christian ministry that places Russian orphans in the homes of loving families to paint a *Pony* that captures the dream-come-true that awaits these children in America, Bonny incorporated the warm red and deep gold colors associated with Russian matruska dolls, along with children's faces peering out with hopeful expressions, doves of peace, and flowers and leaves, into a spectacular artwork that makes a powerful statement about the great freedom in life's journey.

Artist: Bonny
Item: #12209
Running Resin

Available As:

7" Figurine

Retired: July 2007
Retirement #3E/0130

Horsefeathers

Nobody seems to know the derivation of the term "horsefeathers." The most likely explanation is it began as a sanitized variant of "horse-hooey", used to express the view that something is unlikely, about as improbable as that pigs might fly... or that horses should have feathers. By adorning her *Pony* with large, multi-colored feathers, this former art teacher from Texas has given the term a totally new form of expression.

Artist: Jeanne Selby
Item: #12206
Standing Resin

Available As:

6" Figurine   Stationary
Ball Cap
Clothing
Pin/Pendant

Retired: July 2006
Retirement #3E/2530

Fallen Heroes Memorial Pony

There could be no more deserving example, in modern times, of bravery and heroic conduct than the firemen and policemen who pay the ultimate price while keeping the rest of us out of harm's way. Drawing on traditional imagery observed at the funerals of military heroes – a riderless horse with a pair of empty, high-top boots fitted in the stirrups backwards - *The Trail of Painted Ponies*, in collaboration with assorted artisans and craftsmen, created this emotionally stirring and uniquely American tribute to these "Fallen Heroes."

Artist: The Trail of Painted Ponies
Item: #12212
Standing Resin

Available As: Ⓐ Official Autographed Edition

6" Figurine
Picture Frame

Retired: July 2007
Retirement #3E/8202

Painted Lady

"Painted Ladies" is a term often applied to resplendent Victorian houses, brightly painted and expertly restored. Armed with this knowledge, New Mexico artist Barbara Quimby cleverly conceived of a Painted Lady *Pony*, a dolled-up equine celebration of the Victorian spirit as it lives today.

Artist: Barbara Quimby
Item: #12211
Standing Resin

Available As:

6" Figurine

Retired: January 2007
Retirement #2E/7237

Reunion of the Family of Man

Artist Cal Peacock's painted tin "Medicine Horses" have been displayed in such prestigious venues as the Smithsonian Museum. But she considers "Reunion" the "king of the herd." Intricately covered with amazingly detailed imagery and symbols that express empathy and compassion towards our fellow man, and carrying a medicine bundle stocked with bird feathers, Cal's gorgeous *Pony* is an expression of the importance of soulfully connecting with Nature.

Artist: Cal Peacock
Item: #12208
Standing Resin
Native Pony

Available As:

6" Figurine

Retired: January 2008
Retirement #4E/1027

Running with the Ancestors

"The inspiration for this *Pony* comes from prehistoric imagery found on European cave walls, where the grand drawings of horses were both magical and beautiful," says this painter, gallery director and teacher who founded the 5,000 Flowers Project, a national commemoration of 9/11 for healing and harmony through art. Just as contemporary horses echo the drawings of Stone Age artists, so does Carol feel she is linked to Paleolithic artists. "They are my ancestors of creativity and self-expression."

Artist: Carol Adamec
Item: #12210
Running Resin

Available As:

7" Figurine

Rodeo Dreams

A cover artist whose Cowboy paintings massage, twist and tweak traditional concepts of Western Art at the same time they embrace western iconography, Jim lets his *Painted Pony* speak for himself: "I don't want to plough or amble along a trail. I'm not built for dressage and I'm certainly nobody's pet. Give me center stage and I'll give you a show because I'm 'Rodeo Dreams.'"

Artist: Jim Knauf
Item: #12213
Standing Ceramic

Available As:

6" Figurine

Tropical Reef Horse

Sea horses come in an amazing variety of sizes and shapes, and have the ability to instantly change color, camouflaging themselves as seaweed or coral. By brilliantly covering her *Pony* with tropical fish, rendered realistically, overlapping and swimming in all directions, Laurie, a high school art teacher "in an isolated, dusty border town in far West Texas" who scuba dives as a hobby, has created a sea-horse-of-a-different-color.

Artist: Laurie Holman
Item: #12207
Running Resin

Available As:

7" Figurine
Mug

Retired: July 2006
Retirement #2E/8929

Caballito

Monument Valley, Spider Rock, Enchanted Mesa are names that evoke an aura of mystery and legends. Storied sites in the American Southwest, they also shape the dramatic backgrounds for the culturally rich imagery found in the paintings of Mexican/Yaqui artist Amado Pena. Using bold color, striking forms, dynamic composition, and the iconic faces that have distinguished his work for years, Pena has created, with his *Pony*, a tribute to the horses he has known, past and present.

Artist: Amado Pena (Yacqui)
Item: #1525
Running Resin
Native Pony

Available As:

7" Figurine
Mug

Retired: January 2006
Retirement #2E/7207

Epic Horse

Stone tablets have played an important role in the heritage of Chinese culture. Knowing this, Jeffrey Chan, an art designer for Hong Kong movies who also specializes in gift ware design, conceived of a glossy black *Pony* on which a famous poem was carved in a manner that captured the beauty of the art of Chinese calligraphy. The poem, "Orchid Pavilion Preface," was written in AD 352 by Wang Xizhi, one of the most highly respected calligraphers/poets in Chinese history. It is a masterpiece that speaks to the happiness and grace of every living moment.

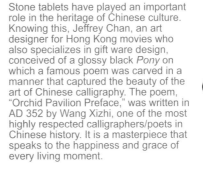

Artist: Jeffrey Chan
Item: #1526
Standing Resin

Available As:

6" Figurine

Retired: January 2006
Retirement #2E/3610

CowPony

With millions of brush strokes masterfully applied, Lori, a western and wildlife artist from Cerrillos, New Mexico, created an original, life-size *Painted Pony* that is proudly exhibited in the Booth Western Art Museum. Upon popular demand, it is now available as a figurine, and as a miniature retains the phenomenal creative power of the original. Sculpted into the *Pony* form as well as painted, a herd of Hereford cows emerge from the swelling muscles of the horse… and hidden among the red-and-whites, a savvy sorrel cowpony.

Artist: Lori Musil
Item: #1584
Standing Resin

Available As:

6" Figurine
Art Print
Mug

Retired: July 2008
Retirement #5E/3748

Incognito

Writes Janee Hughes, a former art teacher and book illustrator from Salem, Oregon, "Biologists are not in agreement about the purpose of a zebra's stripes. Some say the wonderful patterns act as camouflage in the tall grass, but others say the stripes confuse predators. When a lion sees a herd of zebras, it is difficult for her to distinguish one animal from another in order to single out a potential victim. Whichever the case may be, it was great fun creating a herd of Grant's zebras living 'Incognito.'"

Artist: Janee Hughes
Item: #1524
Standing Resin

Available As:

6" Figurine

Retired: January 2008
Retirement #4E/2931

Kokopelli Pony

A sacred figure to Native tribes in the Southwest, the image of Kokopelli, a dancing hunchback playing a flute, appears most frequently in pottery and petroglyphs. A universal minstrel or music spirit who continues to fascinate people, even in our modern technological age, he is given a charming, contemporary interpretation by Joel Nakamura, an Asian-American artist known for his deep knowledge of tribal art and mythology.

Artist: Joel Nakamura
Item: #1508
Running Resin
Native Pony

Available As:

7" Figurine
Ball Cap
Clothing
Picture Frame
Stationary

Retired: January 2008
Retirement #4E/9643

Skyrider

The Hopi believe that when their elders pass on they continue to exist among the clouds, where they protectively watch over their descendants. Wendy, a graduate of the London School of Fine Art who feels her spirit dwells in the deserts, mesas and canyons of the Southwest, has taken this belief to new heights, literally, imagining a *Pony* stampeding across the sky on a glorious journey, collecting the faces of the ancestors and becoming one with the Cloud People.

Artist: Wendy Wells-Bailey
Item: #1509
Running Resin
Native Pony

Available As:

7" Figurine
Pin/Pendant

Retired: January 2006
Retirement #2E/7206

Saguaro Stallion

A former Creative Director with a New York marketing agency, John has enjoyed a successful second career in the arts after moving to Scottsdale, Arizona, where his paintings focus on highly personalized, contemporary interpretations of Nature. His extraordinary rendering of the wondrous effects of a moonrise and sunrise on a stand of saguaro cacti captures John's goal as a painter, which is "to offer new dimensions in how we see our one-of-a-kind desert landscape."

Artist: John Geryak
Item: #1523
Standing Resin

Available As:

6" Figurine
Art Print
Pin/Pendant

Retired: January 2006
Retirement #2E/8401

Willing

Often referred to as one of the most imaginative and compelling ceramists of his generation, Virgil lives and works at the Cochiti Pueblo. He is known as much for taking traditional art forms in cutting-edge directions, as collaborative clothing ventures with New York fashion designer Donna Karan. Tattooed with traditional pottery designs before it was strapped down in black leather and silver spikes, this dramatic re-interpretation of Black Beauty has a mystique, a sensuality and a power that is vintage Virgil Ortiz.

Artist: Virgil Ortiz (Cochiti Pueblo)
Item: #1510
Standing Resin
Native Pony

Available As:

6" Figurine

Retired: January 2006
Retirement #2E/6009

Anasazi Spirit Horse

The intricate black-and-white designs found on Anasazi pottery at Chaco Canyon, which reflect the timeless character of ancient cultures, are the inspiration behind this astounding work of art. Of French and Spanish descent, Robert has also added new dimensions to the art of gourd painting, for which he is respected and collected worldwide. A versatile artist, his horizons are constantly expanding, making him one of the most exciting talents working today.

Artist: Robert Rivera
Item: #1583
Standing Resin
Native Pony

Available As:

6" Figurine
Horse Blanket
Mug
Pin/Pendant

Earth, Wind, and Fire

Read this Cherokee artist's resume and you will understand why he is listed in *Who's Who in American Art*. A Vietnam veteran whose personal philosophy is "Everything is an experiment. That goes for life, for art and for painting a *Pony*," Bill adorned one side of his *Pony* with a portrait of a Plains Indian warrior, and the other with a serene Pueblo scene. Asked for his inspiration, he wrote, "From the Great Spirit and Mother Earth, all things are made."

Artist: Bill Rabbit (Cherokee)
Item: #1545
Running Resin
Native Pony

Available As:

7" Figurine
Lamp
Mug

Retired: January 2007
Retirement #4E/1710

Children's Prayer Pony

In times of great distress, its seems that many Americans turn to prayer, one of the oldest and simplest forms of communication, and truly one of the most powerful and inspiring. In the fall of 2001, at a time when this country was changed forever, children of many faiths from across the United States were invited to share their most prized possessions – their prayers. The compassion, courage, hope and forgiveness they expressed in words and art were collected in a bestselling book – *Children's Prayers for America* – and are shared on this special, heartfelt *Pony* that is an expression of hope in its most humble form.

Artist: Youth of America
Item: #1586
Standing Ceramic

Available As:

6" Figurine
Book: *Children's Prayers for America*

Grandfather's Journey

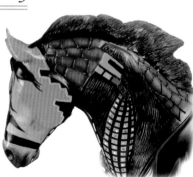

As a young boy growing up on the Hopi mesas of Northern Arizona, Buddy would accompany his grandfather, a Hopi War Chief, as he made his rounds on the back of a donkey checking on the corn fields and herding sheep. Years later, when he developed into a multi-talented artist collected by enthusiasts from around the world, Buddy would credit his grandfather's gift for storytelling with the imagery – Kachina figures, corn maidens, lightning storms – that found their way into his cottonwood carvings, his mystical oil paintings, and his fabulous *Painted Pony*.

Artist: Buddy Tubinaghtewa (Hopi)
Item: #1589
Running Ceramic
Native Pony

Available As:

7" Figurine
Pin/Pendant

Retired: January 2008
Retirement #5E/9232

Kitty Cat's Ball

"Here is what happens when daytime-snoozing feline souls cut loose by the light of the new moon. They jig and waltz, slide a sinuous tango and pound out a mad polka," says Elizabeth, an avid horsewoman, Pony Club mom, and associate member of the American Academy of Equine Art from Huntsville, Alabama. "By day, we only see those half-smiles on snoring kitty faces as they grace our chairs and sofas, or doze in the garden beneath the lilacs. They grin from within as they recall the gavotte from the night before and shiver with delight, dreaming of the next Kitty Cat's Ball."

Artist: Elizabeth Lewis Scott
Item: #1585
Standing Ceramic

Available As:

6" Figurine

Retired: July 2006
Retirement #3E/7112

Thunderbird Suite

Award-winning artist Joel Nakamura is known for his unique style – a blend of folk art and sophisticated iconography – and for his ability to convey stories in an intricate and engaging manner. Joel chose the Thunderbird Myth for his *Pony* because "It was said that a young warrior who was both brave and fast enough to ride his horse under the Thunderbird's great shadow would gain sacred spiritual powers." Joel's paintings have illustrated articles in publications as diverse as *Time* and *Playboy*, and his illustrations were featured in the opening and closing programs of the 2002 Winter Olympics.

Artist: Joel Nakamura
Item: #1582
Standing Resin
Native Pony

Available As:

6" Figurine
Bust
Coasters
Mug
Pin/Pendant

Retired: July 2006
Retirement #3E/5642

Medicine Horse

Recognized by *Southwest Art Magazine* as one of the Top 30 Artists featured in their 30 years of publication, Santa Fe sculptor Star Liana York is as well known for her detailed and sensitive renderings of Native Peoples, as her gift for capturing the spirit of the horse in three-dimensions. With Medicine Horse, she has combined her love and knowledge of people with special relationships to animals by creating a Plains Indian ceremonial horse dressed with a collection of personal objects believed to give the horse's owner power: shields, a lance, a bow, a pipe and assorted amulets and talismans.

Artist: Star Liana York
Item: #1549
Standing Resin
Native Pony

Available As:

6" Figurine   Lamp
9" Figurine   Ornament
Ball Cap   Pin/Pendant
Clothing   Stationary
Picture Frame

Wilderness Roundup

The challenge of creating a wonderful work of art on a large scale, and not allowing her disability to limit her imagination, motivated Mary – wheelchair-bound after suffering a spinal injury during a gymnastics event at age 17 – to paint a *Pony*. Hoping to communicate the "inner connection we share with all living creatures," she rounded up "a dazzling menagerie" of animals "in a changing seasonal environment." Over a year in the making, Mary's *Painted Pony* is an extraordinary achievement that carries this message: "Enjoy her beauty, follow your dreams, and believe in yourself."

Artist: Mitzie Bower
Item: #1588
Standing Ceramic

Available As:

6" Figurine

Retired: July 2007
Retirement #4E/1788

Apple-oosa

Writes the artist, "This *Pony* has a patriotic theme without the usual red, white and blue, stars-and-stripes motif. What is more American than the apple? Hot dogs, baseball and APPLE pie... I rest my case." Working primarily in watercolors and colored pencils, Penny has won a variety of national awards for her still-life paintings – thus the exquisite realism of the apples adorning her Pony's flanks.

Artist: Penny Thomas Simpson
Item: #1596
Standing Ceramic

Available As:

6" Figurine

Retired: January 2006
Retirement #3E/8321

Children of the Garden

This delightful creation by a "tile artist" who designs handmade tiles (www.elkabodetile. com) tells a story of children racing across a magical garden on the back of a magical horse. A place where, in the artist's words, "For a magical moment the 'real world' was not allowed to encroach." On the original *Pony*, the children, bugs and flowers were all formed in clay and fired for hardness before they were hand-painted.

Artist: Connie Garcia
Item: #1538
Running Resin

Available As:

7" Figurine

Retired: September 2004
Retirement #1E/9800

Blue Medicine

A gifted writer and painter, this Cherokee artist wanted her *Pony* to stand not only as a work of art, but an "expression of healing and support for those in need in our community." Adorned with a tribal sash made of leather, shells and beads, decorated with individual handprints of children, Mary worked overtime to complete this "vision and personal prayer" before passing to the other side in the summer of 2003.

Artist: Mary Iron Eyes (Osage)
Item: #1547
Standing Resin
Native Pony

Available As:

6" Figurine   Pin/Pendant
Ball Cap   Stationary
Clothing
Ornament

Dances with Hooves

This Santa Fe folk artist is known for paintings and sculpture that blend Native American and aboriginal styles with a contemporary art sensibility. Ty has blanketed his *Pony* with intricate petroglyph and pictograph designs that seem to float on a rock-like background. "The initial impact is of a textual nature, but upon closer viewing, if one focuses on each design element as a vignette, as a picture all its own, there is much more for the viewer to explore."

Artist: Ty Anderle
Item: #1539
Running Resin
Native Pony

Available As:

7" Figurine

Retired: July 2005
Retirement #2E/5505

Fantastic Fillies

When she was invited to paint a *Pony* that honored the racehorse, Janee, a children's book illustrator, imagined four fast fillies charging down the home stretch, the winner crossing the finish line a nose ahead of the others. The artistry in her design is heightened by the contrasting colors of the horses and the silks of the jockeys set against a midnight-black background, and the determination and courage etched on the faces of the fillies.

Artist: Janee Hughes
Item: #1592
Running Ceramic

Available As:

7" Figurine
Ball Cap
Clothing
Mug

Ghost Horse

A Mohican Indian from northern Wisconsin, Bill has long been one of the most admired figures in the Native American music arena. His album "Ghost Dance" brought him Artist and Album of the Year at the 2000 Native American Music Awards. As talented a painter as he is a songwriter, Bill dug deep within his music and his art to create a spiritual memorial to the massacre at Wounded Knee. With the words to "Ghost Dance" written on the horse beside the portrait of a warrior who fought the White Man but is able to overcome bitterness with faith in a better tomorrow, Bill has created a powerful and original artwork.

Artist: Bill Miller (Mohican)
Item: #1544
Standing Resin
Native Pony

Available As:

6" Figurine	Mug
9" Figurine	Pin/Pendant
Art Print	Plaque
Bust	
Lamp	

Retired: January 2008
Retirement #6E/3894

Floral Pony

Known as a realistic impressionist, this celebrated Mexican artist whose paintings have been exhibited internationally "wanted to deliver the ambiance of the lush vegetation, the bougainvilleas and flowers of the semi-tropical region of southeast Mexico. There you can pick flowers and enjoy plentiful vegetation the year round. The people call their land, 'Eternal Spring.'"

Artist: Noel Espinoza
Item: #1593
Running Ceramic

Available As:

7" Figurine

Retired: July 2005
Retirement #3E/0130

Heavenly Pony

Born in Parral, Chihuahua, Mexico, Noel has devoted his efforts as an artist to sharing a vision of Mexico as a place "as colorful and vivid as a memory." Of his inspiration for his *Pony* he writes, "The nobility and spirit of the Horse is so high and sublime, it led me to take them to heavenly heights in the shape of billowing clouds."

Artist: Noel Espinoza
Item: #1594
Running Ceramic

Available As:

7" Figurine
Ball Cap
Checks
Clothing
Stationary

Retired: July 2008
Retirement #6E/3549

Love As Strong As A Horse

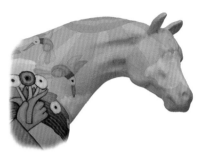

"It was a Cherokee tradition for each family to make and hang a mask in the house for power and protection, to keep in good luck and keep out the bad," says Cherokee artist Jesse Hummingbird, whose paintings of brightly colored, geometric faces have become his signature. "The two couples represent different seasons of life – spring and fall – and are my way of inspiring people to find soulmates with whom they can discover both the strength and beauty of love."

Artist: Jesse Hummingbird (Cherokee)
Item: #1595
Standing Ceramic
Native Pony

Available As:

6" Figurine
Plaque

Retired: July 2005
Retirement #2E/5921

Tewa Horse

Born to a family of artists and craftsmen from the Tesuque Pueblo in New Mexico, Tom (a tribal policeman) wanted to incorporate some of the traditional images that have been handed down from generation to generation, into a design that was contemporary in feeling and rich with symbolism. To do this, he combined various animal abstractions with geometric patterns. The sash represents good fortune. The blanket honors the horse as a bold and strong being. The eagle is a symbol of prosperity. The handprint stands for the loving touch of all creation.

Artist: Tom Tapia (Tesque Pueblo)
Item: #1546
Standing Resin
Native Pony

Available As:

6" Figurine	Ornament
9" Figurine	Pin/Pendant
Ball Cap	Plaque
Clothing	Stationary

Sky of Enchantment

After completing her studies in art, music and fashion design in Hamburg, Germany, Ilse lived in South Africa and Spain before finding paradise in the tiny New Mexico village of Magdalena. There, Ilse writes, "one is blessed with amazingly wide horizons during the day and unrivaled clear views of the stars, milky way and other galaxies at night." Adorned with gold celestial formations that sparkle with semi-precious gems, her *Pony* epitomizes the artist's gift for creating original and enchanting artworks.

Artist: Ilse Magener
Item: #1543
Standing Resin

Available As:

6" Figurine
Bust
Jeweled Gift Box
Mug
Pin/Pendant

Retired: January 2006
Retirement #4E/1547

Wound Up Time On The Range

An architect who wanted to design buildings in the Frank Lloyd Wright tradition – who wanted to work outside the lines, in other words – for many years Roger made his living as a draftsman, translating architectural designs into three-dimensional illustrations. As an escape, he turned to humorous sculpture. By placing a little boy wearing a ten-gallon Stetson on the back of a *Pony* painted to look like a Southwestern landscape, and adding wheels to the base and a cord with a ball at the end, Roger has transformed his *Painted Pony* into a child's pull toy.

Artist: Roger Evans
Item: #1541
Standing Resin

Available As:

6" Figurine

Retired: September 2004
Retirement #1E/8600

Give Me Wings

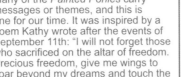

Many of the *Painted Ponies* carry messages or themes, and this is one for our time. It was inspired by a poem Kathy wrote after the events of September 11th: "I will not forget those who sacrificed on the altar of freedom. Precious freedom, give me wings to soar beyond my dreams and touch the stars." As a child of the Southwest, the artist was raised on the San Carlos Apache Reservation and Pine Ridge Sioux Reservation, where her father trained Indian police forces.

Artist: Kathy Morrow
Item: #1471
Running Ceramic

Available As:

7" Figurine
Mug

Retired: July 2005
Retirement #3E/7462

Happy Trails

A former fashion designer from New York City, Nevena wanted to create a horse that reflected the style and costumes worn by Gene Autry and Roy Rogers – 30's and 40's cowboy retro, in other words. It's no mistake that her *Pony* looks as if it is fashioned out of tooled leather, with a vintage saddle cinched on its back. Nevena now lives in El Paso and runs Rocketbuster Boot Company, where some of the wildest cowboy boots you will ever see are handmade.

Artist: Nevena Christi
Item: #1473
Standing Resin

Available As:

6" Figurine	Jeweled Gift Box	Stationary
9" Figurine	Magnet	
Art Print	Mug	
Ball Cap	Ornament	
Clothing	Pin/Pendant	

Go Van Gogh

This tribute to the Dutch master, which combines two of his most recognizable paintings with a humorous rendition of his facial appearance, complete with a missing ear, was created by the sculptor who designed the actual horse forms used in *The Trail of Painted Ponies* art project. As talented at painting as she is at sculpting, Star, who also breeds horses on her New Mexico ranch, knows her horses, and playfully named this piece after the famous racehorse, Go Man Go.

Artist: Star Liana York
Item: #1472
Standing Resin

Available As:

6" Figurine
Magnet
Ornament

Retired: February 2005
Retirement #2E/3200

Mosaic Appaloosa

After distinguishing himself in the field of graphic design in Colorado, Bob established a national name for himself in the fine art field with a signature style that borders on the abstract, yet reflects a true image. "I look at animals and try to strategically place color and design elements that help define their anatomy in a different way." His paintings are part of permanent museum collections in Poland, Finland, Germany and Japan, and were displayed in special shows at the White House and Smithsonian Institution.

Artist: Bob Coonts
Item: #1466
Standing Ceramic

Available As:

6" Figurine
Mug
Pin/Pendant

Retired: March 2004
Retirement #2E/3601

On Common Ground

The unity and harmony of the feminine spirit resound in the vibrant art of California-raised Patricia Wyatt. As with her paintings, her *Pony* tells a story that speaks of the timeless themes of companionship and the collective power, wisdom and beauty of women around the world. Animals and lush flowering plants surround the figures on the artist's *Pony*, emblems of the natural world that pay tribute to the Earth, whose mysterious power awakens us all to life and connects all things.

Artist: Patricia Wyatt
Item: #1470
Standing Ceramic

Available As:

6" Figurine
Checks

Retired: July 2005
Retirement #3E/4906

QuarterHorse

Experimenting with the design and dimensionality of an actual quarter, and the sculptural form of the horse breed that goes by the same name, this former art director for a national magazine found the coin's features lent themselves to the existing contours of the horse. "I particularly like how the eagle's wings flow into the horse's mane and tail," Kathy says. "By focusing on the eagle and selected words of a quarter, it also offers an opportunity to reflect an additional theme of national allegiance." A silver finish, appearing "aged" for contrast, gives the appearance of the horse a feeling of having been crafted from metal.

Artist: Kathy Morawski
Item: #1475
Running Resin

Available As:

7" Figurine
9" Figurine
Magnet
Mug
Ornament

Retired: September 2004
Retirement #2E/6800

Patrol Horse

Although there is a historical relationship between the horse and law enforcement – think Royal Canadian Mounted Police and Texas Rangers – the partnership today is limited primarily to search and rescue missions and crowd control. Nevertheless, out of respect for tradition, the creative team of Dwayne and Ginger Ulibarri has created a "poster mount," smartly tacking up their *Pony* in an officer's uniform, polished black boots, campaign hat, mirrored shades, and the classic imperturbable expression that makes you wonder if he has eyes in the back of his head. Nothing is going to rock this *Pony's* world!

Artist: Dwayne & Ginger Ulibarri
Item: #1457
Standing Resin

Available As:

6" Figurine
Magnet
Ornament

Retired: July 2005
Retirement #2E/2888

Renewal of Life

Natasha's travels abroad and around the Southwest have fueled her love for interpreting the "magical landscapes" she has witnessed. A dawn seen through mists hovering over the Rio Grande River that flows through a bird sanctuary in Southern New Mexico, inspired this work of art. Whether she is painting on a canvas or a *Pony*, this artist has a unique ability to create a spiritual luminescence that invites the viewer to enter a meditative space that seems to live inside her art.

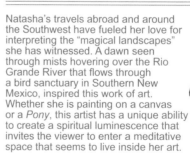

Artist: Natasha Isenhour
Item: #1467
Running Ceramic

Available As:

7" Figurine
Checks
Pin/Pendant

Retired: January 2007
Retirement #5E/1202

Rosie the Apparoosa

This work of radiant and unusual beauty was created by a New Mexico artist nationally known for using the floral form as a means of exploring the relationships of color and value in painting. Riotous displays of multi-hued roses in bud and bloom, with not a single flower repeated, sprout from earthen hooves and thorny branch-covered legs. "I dubbed her Rosie," says Marianne, "and as she departed her first stable on a warm day in May, three real rose bushes by my studio door bloomed more profusely than any past spring."

Artist: Marianne Hornbuckle
Item: #1469
Standing Ceramic

Available As:

6" Figurine

Retired: March 2004
Retirement #2E/0577

Unity

It was not solely for his grand vision – combining imagery of the early Spanish explorers who brought the horse to America five centuries ago, with representations of the Native tribes whose culture was radically changed by the horse – that this former fashion photographer turned pop artist received the award for the most ambitious *Pony*. To give his artwork monumental impact, Georges Monfils covered it with over a million and a half tiny Indian seed beads, applied one at a time! So impressive was the outcome, which took the artist over 1,400 hours to complete, that it was nominated for the Guinness Book of World Records.

Artist: Georges Monfils
Item: #1468
Standing Ceramic
Native Pony

Available As:

6" Figurine

Retired: September 2004
Retirement #2E/1945

Sequintial: A Sequine

Nancy, who has a Fine Arts Degree from the Kansas City Art Institute, is known as a collage artist who artfully incorporates found objects into her artwork, usually in some sort of repeating pattern. "I can't throw out junk mail without first removing the cancelled stamps," she says, by way of explaining how she came to cover her horse with 77,000 iridescent and multi-colored sequins.

Artist: Nancy Fleming
Item: #1474
Standing Resin

Available As:

6" Figurine
Magnet
Ornament

Retired: September 2004
Retirement #2E/0800

Vi's Violet Vision

There are personal reasons why this artist prefers to be known by the moniker, Mister E. They are suggested in the poem he provided in place of a biography. "Adopted here, adopted there. So many names, not one my own. A father a day, not one there to stay." Though his identity remains a "mystery," his talent is evident and extraordinary. From award-winning oil portraits to comic book illustrations, with this tribute to Carousel Horses, this artist is making a new name for himself.

Artist: Mister E
Item: #1476
Running Resin

Available As:

7" Figurine
Magnet
Ornament
Pin/Pendant

Retired: July 2006
Retirement #3E/9282

Boot Scootin' Horsey

Carla Slusher lives on a ranch in southeastern New Mexico, where she paints to country-and-western music. As her vision of a dancing horse wearing a cowboy hat, jeans, and color-coordinated boots, ready for a night on the town, neared completion, it so happened her favorite radio station played the song "Boot Scootin' Boogie." This is how she came up with the name for her *Pony*, which has attitude with a capital "A."

Artist: Carla Slusher
Item: #1454
Standing Resin

Available As:

6" Figurine
Magnet
Ornament

Retired: March 2004
Retirement #2E/4520

Fireman Pony

Horses were an important part of the early Fire Services, hauling water wagons to the scene of burning buildings and houses. Cleverly, and with humor and affection, Dwayne and Ginger Ulibarri have captured that sense of the horse as a fireman's best friend. As well as being artists in their own right, the Ulibarri's operated the Albuquerque foundry where the *Painted Pony* forms were cast.

Artist: Dwayne & Ginger Ulibarri
Item: #1453
Standing Resin

Available As:

6" Figurine
Magnet
Ornament

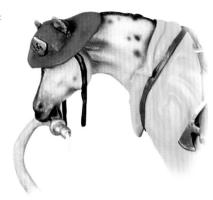

Retired: July 2005
Retirement #3E/8046

Caballo Brillante

Roger Montoya is a nationally recognized renaissance figure, as well known for his dance performances as his landscape paintings. He served as Artistic Director of this *Pony*, assembling a team of some 50 people, ranging in age from 5 to 81, from a New Mexico village to collect glass and ceramic shards from nearby riverbeds and old dumps, and arrange them into a mosaic that danced with light and color.

Artist: Roger Montoya
Item: #1456
Standing Resin

Available As:

6" Figurine
Magnet
Ornament

Retired: January 2007
Retirement #5E/4734

Five Card Stud

Artistic inspiration comes in many forms. Drawing on her experience as a secondary art teacher, Carlsbad artist Gerri Mattson gave herself an assignment. She made a list of words that related to horses, and then began to sketch out corresponding ideas. The word "Stud" prompted an association with poker, which led to a horse fancifully adorned with gaming, casino, and lottery images.

Artist: Gerri Mattson
Item: #1459
Standing Ceramic

Available As:

7" Figurine
Mug

Retired: January 2008
Retirement #5E/1533

Karuna

Says actress and animal-lover Ali MacGraw, "I chose to make a fantasy creature, inspired by the fabulous horses of Central Asia, that would inspire compassion for all God's creatures, great and small, all over the world. With Karuna, which means "Compassion" in Sanskrit, Ali demonstrates that her talent and creativity extend far beyond the silver screen.

Artist: Ali MacGraw
Item: #1455
Standing Resin

Available As:

6" Figurine
Magnet
Ornament

Retired: March 2004
Retirement #2E/3488

Motorcycle Mustang

A second-generation lover and owner of motorcycles, David Losoya, an airbrush artist from Artesia, New Mexico, wanted to create a creature that "If I was a biker in the 19th century, I would ride." With the help of friends and family, he molded many parts of real motorcycles onto his horse, including mufflers, a kickstarter, leather saddlebags, and chains instead of reins. This *Pony* rumbles!

Artist: David Losoya
Item: #1450
Standing Resin

Available As:

6" Figurine   Ornament
Ball Cap   Pin/Pendant
Clothing
Coasters
Magnet

Lightning Bolt Colt

In Lakota Sioux mythology the horse is a "Thunder Being," who brings storms to Mother Earth. With storms come rain and change. With this in mind, Choctaw artist Dyanne Strongbow, imagined a thunderstorm centered in the horse's hindquarters, breaking up as it moved toward his head into the sunny skies of a new day.

Artist: Dyanne Strongbow (Choctaw)
Item: #1461
Running Ceramic
Native Pony

Available As:

7" Figurine   Pin/Pendant
Art Prints
Coasters
Mug

Navajo Blanket Pony

After receiving a degree from the Boston Museum School of Fine Art, New Englander Barbara Tomasko Quimby moved to Wagon Mound, New Mexico, where she fell in love with the native cultures and people of the West. Admiring the artistry displayed by Navajo women weaving fabulous blankets with thread on loom, she was moved to create this tribute, incorporating the color and design "of day and night, of deserts flat and mountain height."

Artist: Barbara Tomasko Quimby
Item: #1464
Standing Ceramic
Native Pony

Available As:

6" Figurine
Pin/Pendant

Retired: March 2004
Retirement #2E/7742

Route 66 Horse

Ellen Sokoloff considers herself an "American painter." Her artwork preserves scenes from an earlier time in our country's history. Childhood memories of western trips along historic Route 66, America's "Mother Road," inspired the collage of diners, motels, gas stations and tourist attractions that embellish her *Painted Pony*.

Artist: Ellen Sokoloff
Item: #1460
Standing Ceramic

Available As:

6" Figurine
Coasters
Mug

Retired: July 2005
Retirement #4E/1107

War Pony

Comanche artist Rance Hood is one of the most recognized names in Southwest Art. His paintings, known for their drama and authenticity, hang in museums and corporate collections. The opportunity to recreate a traditional war pony, complete with a buffalo pelt saddle, lance-and-shield, arrows and feathers became the pinnacle piece of his distinguished career.

Artist: Rance Hood (Comanche)
Item: #1452
Standing Resin
Native Pony

Available As:

6" Figurine	Clothing	Picture Frame
9" Figurine	Lamp	Pin/Pendant
Art Print	Magnet	Plaque
Ball Cap	Mug	Stationary
Bust	Ornament	

Spirit War Pony

The Santa Fe artist Tavlos is credited with originating the famous howling coyote imagery that became the trademark of Southwest art in the '80s. Known for his bold colors and vivid designs, he took a pop art approach to the Native American tradition of painting their horses, giving his *Pony* a turquoise coat and decorating it with dazzling accents.

Artist: Tavlos
Item: #1462
Standing Ceramic
Native Pony

Available As:

6" Figurine
Coasters
Mug
Pin/Pendant

Retired: February 2005
Retirement #3E/8478

Wildfire

Anyone who has lived in the West knows firsthand about the awesome power and unpredictability of a wildfire. As well, anyone who has ridden horses knows they too are powerful and can be unpredictable. Carlsbad artist Gerri Mattson has creatively combined these two natural forces into a single dynamic image in which a forest fire raging out of control and horse stand together in single artform.

Artist: Gerri Mattson
Item: #1458
Standing Ceramic

Available As:

6" Figurine

Retired: March 2004
Retirement #2E/9117

Special Collections & Editions

Special Collections and Editions stand apart from the regular twice-a-year release of *Painted Ponies* figurines.

Some, such as the Holiday Collections, are released annually in conjunction with an ornament that comes in a collectible tin.

Some are announced as limited editions at the start and include distinguishing features such as a brass medallion, an example being the Four Seasons Collection.

Then there are the Exclusive Editions, which are only available through a specially committed retailer of *Painted Ponies,* such as Dillard's Department Stores, or an entire country, such as Canada and Australia.

Finally, there are the Official Autographed Editions. Offered exclusively through *The Official Trail of Painted Ponies Website Store*, this edition consists of a limited number of artist-autographed, artist-numbered figurines that are authenticated with a signed Certificate of Authenticity.

For more information about all of these editions:
www.trailofpaintedponies.com

*Holiday Figurine
with Ornament Tin*

*Limited Editions give
"Horsepower" to your collection!*

*Four Seasons Collection Figurine
with Medallion*

*Exclusive Edition
Available in Canada*

*Official Autographed Edition
with Certificate of Authenticity*

Holiday Collections

Four Holiday-themed *Painted Ponies* figurines and ornaments are crafted each year. The highly anticipated Holiday Collections, which are unveiled on June 1, have created for collectors both a new family gift-giving tradition as well as another way to decorate their homes that celebrates the season.

Happy Holiday's...
Ho Ho Ho!

Peppermint Twist

Let it Snow

"During the holidays as a child, all I wanted for Christmas was a big fluffy snowfall so I could build a perfect snowman, decorated with a hat and scarf, sticks for arms, a carrot for a nose, and big black buttons of coal. Living in the Midwest, coal wasn't readily available, so mom always had a tin full of buttons for the occasion." Now, as an adult, this Iowa artist still finds something magical about "big fluffy snowfalls," and created a *Pony* designed to take everyone back to a time and place where they too waited with anticipation for the holidays and the chance to build that perfect snowman.

Artist: Vickie Knepper
Item: #12285
Walking Resin

Available As:

7" Figurine
Ornament

Twas the Night Before Christmas

With a sleigh full of toys and reindeer so quick, a bowl full of jelly, it could only be St. Nick.

He hopped into the seat of his apple red sleigh, calling out to his reindeer, "Up, up and away!"

Dashing through the night with a bag full of toys, he brought happiness and hope to every girl and boy.

The artist who created this wonderful *Holiday Pony* has worked as a graphics illustrator for National Geographic Magazine.

Artist: Johanna Enriquez
Item: #12287
Standing Resin

Available As:

6" Figurine
Ornament

Peppermint Twist

According to legend, candy canes were created to symbolize Jesus, their shape representing the letter J. But to most people the hard, cane-shaped candy, traditionally with red and white stripes and flavored with peppermint, is as much an ornament as a confection – a sweet treat to munch as well as to decorate a tree.

The artist who created this tasty *Holiday Pony* hails from Alabama keeps out a bowl of candy canes and swirls at Christmas time… and often long past.

Artist: Leslie Gates
Item: #12286
Walking Resin

Available As:

7" Figurine
Ornament

Wooden Toy Horse

This delightful *Holiday Pony* captures a classic Christmas moment of a jolly Santa sitting at a table in his cozy house at the North Pole, reviewing his naughty or nice list, checking it twice, and from time to time letting out a "Ho, ho, ho!" as images of children's wishes – toy trains, biplanes, dolls and cars – fill his head.

The artist who created this captivating *Holiday Pony* has worked as a graphics illustrator for National Geographic Magazine.

Artist: Johanna Enriquez
Item: #12288
Standing Resin

Available As:

6" Figurine
Ornament

Feliz Navidad

Snow and reindeer are a traditional part of winter holiday celebrations, but in warmer climates, the festive season is known for other things. This happy *Pony* embodies the cultural traditions of our neighbor to the south, Mexico – music, dancing, the Posada, Poinsettia, piñata, and most of all, joyful children!

Artist: Janee Hughes
Item: #12259
Standing Resin

Available As:

6" Figurine
Ornament

Penguin Express

Penguins, the subject of several popular movies, have achieved star power. Their current appeal almost rivals the appeal that the horse has to people. Watching them waddle and slide around the ice and snow of the Antarctic in their "tuxedos," it's easy to see why. So it was natural for Idaho painter Maria Ryan to combine the two, and to imagine a scene in which a *Holiday Pony* transports a penguin family across the ice in a snow storm.

Artist: Maria Ryan
Item: #12258
Running Resin

Available As:

7" Figurine
Ornament

Gingerbread Pony

Come Christmas in artist Lynn Bean's home, baking gingerbread cookies was a cherished tradition. "As my mother rolled out the dough, my sister and I would press the cookie cutter designs of stars, bells, animals and people. The yummy smell of gingerbread baking would fill the kitchen. After the cookies cooled we would add frosting and decorations. Then we would eat the rejects, making enough to take to Grandma's house or for friends at school." With these magical memories in mind, Lynn designed a *Pony* of frosted cookies and candies, complete with a Christmas country scene of an old barn and a gingerbread family leading a pony among the trees and bells of the holiday.
Artist: Lynn Bean
Item: #12256
Running Resin

Available As:

7" Figurine
Ornament

Poinsettia Pony

Along with the traditional Christmas tree, Poinsettias, with their large and showy leaves, are a staple of the holidays. Indeed, when visiting friends or going to holiday parties, the choice gift to bring the hostess is a pretty Poinsettia plant in full bloom. This season Idaho painter Maria Ryan has created a different kind of Poinsettia as a gift… which is accompanied by this short verse: "Somehow, not only at Christmas but all the long year through… the joy that you give to others is the joy that comes back to you."

Artist: Maria Ryan
Item: #12257
Running Resin

Available As:

7" Figurine
Ornament

Crystal

She has come to love the desert landscapes of Arizona, but this immigrant artist from the Ukraine says "I miss the glistening of the snow on sunny winter days, the diamond sparkling beauty of frozen forests; the incredible patterns of fantasy plants and animals that crystallize on winder windows." Inspired by those wonderland memories, and painting in the 18th century style of country people who would beautify their homes with floral paintings on the walls that included birds of paradise and swirls of silver lace, Olena has created a gorgeous tribute to the magical beauty of winter around the world.

Artist: Olena Kalayda
Item: #12238
Walking Resin

Available As:

7" Figurine
Horse Blanket
Ornament
Snow Globe

Polar Express

The original Santa Claus, St. Nicholas, is said to have delivered gifts to children while riding a magnificent white horse. Flying reindeer are OK, but this gifted artist from the Pacific Northwest asks us to imagine what it would look like "if Santa still delivered toys from the back of a beautiful white horse."

Artist: J.E. Speight
Item: #12237
Running Resin

Available As:

7" Figurine
Ornament
Snow Globe

Frosty

The magic in that old silk hat is always welcome around the holidays… With that in mind, artist/writer Janee Hughes livens up the season with a *Pony* that carries a crowd of jolly, happy, dancing snowmen on its back who, as the children say, "can laugh and play just the same as you and me."

Artist: Janee Hughes
Item: #12236
Standing Resin

Available As:

6" Figurine
Ornament
Snow Globe

Silver Bells

"A silver-gray horse in fancy harness is the perfect representative of the beauty of the season," according to Oregon painter/writer Janee Hughes. After looking at her *Pony*, she asks us to close our eyes and imagine, "The tinkle of his sleigh bells – the only sound emerging from the deep quiet of softly falling snow. Mane flying, tail waving, and feathered legs lifted high, as he invites everyone to go for a ride!"

Artist: Janee Hughes
Item: #12235
Walking Resin

Available As:

7" Figurine
Ornament
Snow Globe

Big Red

A culturally diverse and worldly fellow, Santa has many interpretations and different names: Father Christmas in England, Kriss Kringle in Germany, Pere Noel in France, Saint Nicholas in the Netherlands. But almost universally he is a plump and jolly figure who dresses in red, carries a bulging sack on his back, and brings gifts to good children. Destined to become a classic, "Big Red" is a lavish and loving example of how the symbol of Christmas is no longer just a decorated Christmas tree, but is now all about artistic expression.

Artist: The Trail of Painted Ponies
Item: #12215
Standing Resin

Available As:

6" Figurine
Ornament

Retired: July 2007
Retirement #2E/5009

Happy Holidays

Think Christmas on the ranch... tacking up your trusty horse with a seasonal saddle blanket, tying on stockings instead of saddlebags and buckling up a breast collar that tinkles like sleigh bells... then riding over to the neighbor's cabin to share hearth and home. Could there be a better way to spread holiday cheer? Joy Stueurwald and Mike Dowdall, designers at Westland Giftware, didn't think so when they created "Happy Holidays."

Artist: Mike Dowdall & Joy Steuerwald
Item: #12217
Standing Resin

Available As:

6" Figurine
Ornament

Deck the Halls

Imagine a *Painted Pony* spruced up as a Christmas tree in fresh greenery, decorated with vintage Christmas ornaments and red bows, strung with tinsel garland and multi-colored lights, and posed on a Christmas skirt that sparkles like a magic carpet. That's what the Design Department of *The Trail of Painted Ponies* had in mind when it created a seasonal selection that captures the Christmas magic expressed in the carol, "Deck the Halls."

Artist: The Trail of Painted Ponies
Item: #12216
Standing Resin

Available As:

6" Figurine
Ornament

Retired: July 2007
Retirement #3E/1401

Reindeer Roundup

In hopes of drawing Santa's sleigh through the Christmas sky like the red-nosed Rudolph, this reindeer-wannabe tried to disguise the fact he was a *Painted Pony* by rounding up a set of antlers and throwing a gaudy saddle blanket on his back that lights up the night with stars. Even if he doesn't get a chance to pull Santa's sleigh, he will bring cheer to the season, and make this a memorable Christmas for those who find him prancing under their tree.

Artist: Mike Dowdall & Joy Steuerwald
Item: #12218
Running Resin

Available As:

7" Figurine
Clothing
Ornament

Christmas Clydesdale

Imagine a Christmas sled full of laughing children being pulled down a snowy city street by a massive, but reliable draft horse, festively adorned with a holly wreath… and you have the inspiration for this Christmas *Pony*. Mike, the Art Director at Westland Giftware, has been in the design industry for over 25 years. Joy is a designer and a Product Development Coordinator at Westland.

Artist: Mike Dowdall & Joy Steuerwald
Item: #12203
Standing Resin

Available As:

6" Figurine
Ornament
Snow Globe

Nutcracker

Drawing on imagery from the 19th century Russian ballet, "The Nutcracker", Janee, a former art teacher from Salem, Oregon, has created a strikingly original and theatrical tribute to this Christmas tradition, as perfect in detail as a Faberge egg. The *Nutcracker Pony* is about magic and music and family and celebration.

Artist: Janee Hughes
Item: #12201
Running Ceramic

Available As:

7" Figurine
Ornament
Snow Globe

Golden Girl

In a serene and majestic setting among heavenly clouds, the angelic "Golden Girl" watches the hustle and bustle of life below… and wishes for Peace on Earth. A designer at Westland Giftware, Joy is a published children's book illustrator and has also worked in the children's educational CD-ROM industry.

Artist: Joy Steuerwald
Item: #12204
Standing Resin

Available As:

6" Figurine
Ornament
Snow Globe

Retired: February 2006
Retirement #1E/8400

Snowflake

Remembering Christmas Eve snowfalls at her grandparent's lake cottage, watching big lazy flakes drift through the night sky and "dreaming of the pony that Santa would surely bring this year," moved this professional musician and bookstore owner from Sunnyside, Washington, to create this new Christmas classic.

Artist: Judith Fudenski
Item: #12202
Running Resin

Available As:

7" Figurine
Ornament
Jeweled Gift Boxes
Snow Globe

FOUR SEASONS
COLLECTION

*T*he *Trail of Painted Ponies* is celebrating the beauty of the four
seasons with a special collection of four *Painted Ponies*. Spring,
Summer, Fall and Winter are each honored with a different *Pony*.
Each of these unique beauties captures a charming aspect of a different
season of the year and is part of a limited edition of 20,000 castings. A
beautiful brass medallion graces the base with the title of the *Pony* and the
edition number.

Celebrate the Four Seasons....

THE TRAIL OF
PAINTED PONIES
FOUR SEASONS COLLECTION
SPRING
TIP TOE THROUGH THE TULIPS
X / 20,000

Tip-Toe Through The Tulips

Tip-Toe Through the Tulips

This *Painted Pony* combines the artist's love of both horses and flowers. A vibrant black-and-white Appaloosa steps carefully through a colorful garden of springtime tulips. Look closely and you will see the inspiration behind the title....

Artist: Leslie Gates
Item: #12269
Running Resin

Available As: Ⓐ Official Autographed Edition

7" Figurine

Autumn Dancer

When summer ends, autumn comes... a time of harvest and gathering together to sing and dance, a second spring when every leaf becomes a flower, the occasion for long walks under old great trees that will soon become flaming torches leading the way to winter.

Artist: Mike Dowdall
Item: #12271
Running Resin

Available As: Ⓐ Official Autographed Edition

7" Figurine

Summer Ballet

You know that summer has arrived when you look out the window and see hummingbirds, like jewels with quivering, iridescent wings, darting swiftly and sweetly around the garden, hovering long enough to dip their long, slender bills into the hearts of flowers, then flashing away in a fairy-like aerial dance that seems performed just for you.

Artist: Joyce Kennedy
Item: #12270
Walking Resin

Available As: Ⓐ Official Autographed Edition

7" Figurine

Winter Song

Frosty nights, snowy days and warm hearts make these little birds, perched among pine branches sprinkled with glistening, white, crystal snow, sing their sweet Winter Song.

Artist: Lynn Bean
Item: #12272
Walking Resin

Available As: Ⓐ Official Autographed Edition

7" Figurine

Exclusive Editions

On special occasions, *The Trail* has agreed to work with a company that is doing an exceptional job representing *Painted Ponies*, and create an exclusive figurine. Dillard's Department Stores is an example. It has done such a fine job with *Painted Ponies* figurines that it has been honored with an Exclusive Edition *Painted Pony* twice.

The Trail has done this on only six occasions, and has found that their scarcity has made these *Painted Ponies* particularly attractive to collectors who seek them out as if on a treasure hunt.

The place to go to find out more about the Exclusive Editions is: www.trailofpaintedponies.com

Follow The Trail... It's A Treasure Hunt!

Kindred Spirits

Reflections of Australia

The inspiration behind the Australian *Painted Pony* draws on traditional themes of Aboriginal Australia, a culture that has historically faced many hardships and challenges, but in many ways forms the foundation of Australia today. The design is a masterful fusion of Aboriginal symbols and markings, images of native animals, representations of the landscape, and the colors of the national flag that celebrates Australia's diversity and multicultural nature.

Born and raised in Papua New Guinea by adoptive Australian parents, the artist moved at a young age to Brisbane, Queensland.

Artist: Emma Robinson
Item: #11527
Running Ceramic

Available As:

7" Figurine

Maple Leaf Pony

The Canadian Horse originated from horses sent to Quebec by King Louis XIV in the late 1600s. Adapting to extreme conditions and sparse feed, it evolved into a hardy easy-keeper that, according to lore, is capable of generating "more power per hundred pounds of body weight than horses of any other breed." Most commonly black in color, good-natured and truly versatile, it is a natural "canvas" for a horse that represents all of Canada. Covered with 14 maple leaves - signifying 10 provinces and 3 territories that are unified by a large maple leaf draped over its back - and running above a map of Canada, this exclusive *Painted Pony* was created by a Canadian artist who runs a small boarding and riding facility named Justa Lil Ranch in the far northern reaches of Alberta.
Artist: Jennifer Kessler
Item: #11298
Running Resin

Available As:

7" Figurine
Ornament

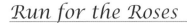

Kindred Spirits

"Like many Native People, I have a deep love and respect for animals and what we can learn from them, says this self-taught artist from Loon Lake, Washington. Guided by this belief, she has imagined a *Pony* standing in a mountaintop meadow, surrounded by animal friends, each with a lesson to teach. The buffalo represents renewal. The Eagle sees the world with clarity. The bear stands for power. The wolf is a model for cooperation. The mouse, though small, was looked upon by traditional tribes as a pathfinder. "And the circle around the *Pony's* eye speaks to the improved vision that comes from using animal wisdom to improve our daily lives."

Finalist:
Native Art of Horse Painting Competition

Artist: Debbie Hughbanks
Item: #12268
Walking Ceramic
Native Pony

Available As:

7" Figurine
Puzzle

Run for the Roses

The Kentucky Derby is the most prestigious horse race in America. In a matter of seconds, hopes can be dashed, dreams can be realized, and fortunes can be won or lost. The outcome is never sure until those final moments when horses and jockeys thunder down the home stretch. Equestrian artist extraordinaire, Janee Hughes, has captured the excitement of the race for the finish line in the bright colors and straining horses and riders... with the roses as a reminder of the importance of the outcome.

Artist: Janee Hughes
Item: #12239
Running Ceramic

Available As:

7" Figurine

The Phoenix Pony

The Ancient Ones called these deserts home. Then, around 1400 A.D., for unknown reasons, they mysteriously disappeared. Hundreds of years later, a new town would arise from the ruins that would be appropriately named "Phoenix" after the fabulous mythical bird of brilliant scarlet and gold plumage that was said to have perished in flames, only to arise from the ashes. Created by Arizona artist Wendy Wells-Bailey, "The Phoenix Pony" stands as a tribute to a timeless and a beautiful city that shares its name, and to the human capacity for renewal and rebirth.

Artist: Wendy Wells-Bailey
Item: #11568
Running Resin

Available As:

7" Figurine

High Desert Horse Feathers

Native American influences have been a part of Kathy Morrow's life since childhood; she was raised on the San Carlos Apache and Pine Ridge Sioux Indian Reservations, where her father organized Indian police departments. Many of her paintings reflect Native American legends. With her design, the white plume of an Eagle feather stretches along each side of the Pony, forming the perfect background for a series of four painted horses that represent the rainbow of mankind – black man, yellow man, red man, and white man. The total effect is an image of harmony at its best.

Artist: Kathy Morrow
Item: #11254
Standing Resin
Native Pony

Available As:

6" Figurine
Puzzle

Official Autographed Editions

Official Autographed Editions

With every release of new figurines *The Trail of Painted Ponies* creates an Official Autographed Edition. This edition is limited in number and available only through *The Trail of Painted Ponies Official Website Store*.

Each figurine is individually autographed and hand-numbered by the artist who created the original *Painted Pony*. It is accompanied by a Certificate of Authenticity, also signed and numbered by the artist, to guarantee authenticity.

Autographed Editions are prized by serious collectors looking for ways to enhance the value of their *Painted Ponies* collections.

The Official Autographed Editions are available exclusively through *The Trail of Painted Ponies* at: www.trailofpaintedponies.com

Enhance your collection with Autographed Editions!

"Dream Warriors"
Official Autographed Edition

Ross Lampshire Signing the Certificates of Authenticity for "Dream Warriors"

THE TRAIL OF
PAINTED PONIES
1E/ 2,889
Item No. 12233 Dream Warriors
Artist: Ross Lampshire
™ and © 2006 The Trail of Painted Ponies, Inc.
Handcrafted in China
1/250
Item No. 12233

Autographed Edition Base

Official Autographed Editions Release Dates

Four Seasons Collection 2008
Edition of 250
Tip-Toe Through The Tulips
Summer Ballet
Autumn Dancer
Winter Song

Summer 2008
Edition of 150
Wounded Knee
Runs the Bitterroot
For Spacious Skies
Stagecoach Pony
Rolling Thunder
Kachina Pony
Bunkhouse Bronco
Sundancer

Winter 2008
Edition of 250
Wish Upon A Star
Twilight Hunters
Trail of Honor
Serenity
Prairie Horizon
Indian Summer
Dreamwalker
Crazy Horse

Summer 2007
Edition of 250
Sacred Reflections of Time
Wie-Tou
Northern Lights
Boot Camp
Ceremonial Pony
Stardust
Navajo Black Beauty

Winter 2007
Edition of 250
Bedazzled
Cheyenne Painted Rawhide
Copper Enchantment
Fancy Dancer
Native Jewel Pony
Silverado
Sounds of Thunder
Viva Las Vegas

Summer 2006
Edition of 250
Blondes
Dog and Pony Show
Dream Warriors
Horse With No Name
Many Tribes
Spirits of the Northwest
Super Charger

Winter 2006
Edition of 250
Silver Lining
Fetish Pony
Woodland Hunter
Horsepower to Burn

Philanthropic Editions
Winter 2006
The Gary Avey Heard Museum Fund
Edition of 100
Native People's Pony
The Magician

Summer 2005
Hall of Flame Firefighter Museum
Edition of 343
Fallen Heroes Memorial Pony

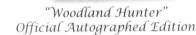

"Woodland Hunter"
Official Autographed Edition

Kevin Kilhoffer
Autographing "Woodland Hunter"

Paint Your Own Pony Kits

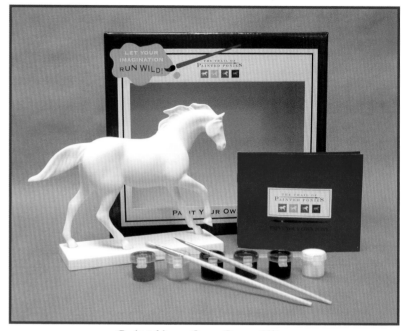

As a way of giving everyone who loves *Painted Ponies* the opportunity to discover their "inner *Painted Pony* artist," *The Trail* created a *Paint Your Own Pony Kit*. Each kit contains a blank, resin, running, figurine-sized Pony, two paint brushes, six acrylic paint pots, and an instruction booklet with helpful tips from *Official Painted Pony Artists*.

Since their introduction, *Paint Your Own Pony Kits* have become a gift that keeps on giving. They invite creative expression in everybody who buys one for themselves, and encourage creativity when given as gifts to others. Collectors love adding a personally *Painted Pony* to their collections!

The *Paint Your Own Pony Kits* have also received a big welcome in school art classes, where teachers use them to jump-start the creative process in students.

Philanthropic organizations have effectively used *Paint Your Own Pony Kits* to increase awareness and raise funds by inviting celebrities to paint Kit Ponies that are sold at auction.

Workshops are being hosted by *Official Trail of Painted Ponies Artists*, in an effort to nourish the "inner *Painted Pony* artist" in everyone! Check the Calendar of Events on *The Trail of Painted Ponies Official Website* to find a detailed listing of workshops across America.

Look for more arts and crafts from *The Trail of Painted Ponies* in the future!

Paint Your Own Pony Kit
Includes: Paints, Brushes and Instruction Booklet

Thankful Spirit
Vicky Wiley

Artist Ross Lampshire
Oakview Elementary School

Artist Lori Musil
Dillard's Workshop in Arizona

Artist Buddy Tubinaghtewa
The Trail Gallery Workshop

Father and Daughter
The Kentucky Horse Park

Winter Encounter
Fabienne Leydecker

Mom, Baseball and Apple Pie
Virgil Stephens

Pueblo Pottery Pony
Ross Lampshire

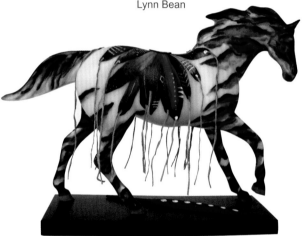

Dragonfly Pony
Lynn Bean

Artists Paint Their Own Ponies

Trail of Painted Ponies artists are turning the *Paint Your Own Pony Kits* into works of fine art! *Official Trail of Painted Ponies Artists* create custom *Painted Ponies* from these kits, which they sell directly to collectors in the *Custom Painted Ponies Corral* on *The Trail of Painted Ponies Official Website*.

www.trailofpaintedponies.com

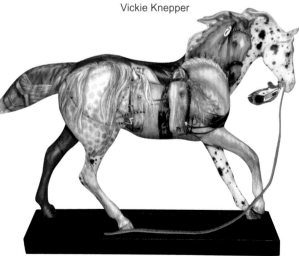

Tribal Paint
Vickie Knepper

Rockin Horse Round-up
Oakview Elementary School

Full Battle Dress
P. Alexander Roibol
(New Mexico Pueblos)

The Comedian
Gene Dieckhoner

Cowgirls Rule
Sue Sizemore

Road to the Horse
Lori Musil

Petrogyph Pony
Lynn Bean

Thunder Horse
Barbara Brown

New!

New Collectibles

*T*he *Trail* continues with more remarkable collectibles, and *Painted Ponies* gifts for all. From our newest collectible - *Painted Ponies* Jeweled Gift Boxes - to ornaments and lamps, to picture frames and limited edition art prints, you can add unique Western accents to your interior decor, or you can give a gift that will be treasured forever.

The Trail of Painted Ponies announce a stunning new collection of Jeweled Gift Boxes. Cast in pewter and beautifully enameled, they are decorated with Austrian crystals and 24K gold or fine silver plating.

Horseshoe Charm

Each Painted Ponies Jeweled Gift Box opens and contains an Austrian crystal Horseshoe Charm to bring good luck to each collector!

Copper Enchantment

Stardust

Native Jewel Pony

Example of an open Jeweled Gift Box

Year of the Horse

Photo Finish

Happy Trails

Snowflake

Sky of Enchantment

A

THE TRAIL OF
PAINTED PONIES

Collectibles & More

Surround yourself with beauty from *The Trail of Painted Ponies*. Or, give a gift that will be treasured forever.

Happy Decorating, Happy Trails!

B
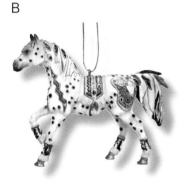

. . . .

Please note that collectibles featuring (R) have been retired.

C
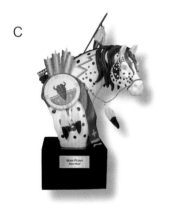

A *New* Exquisitely crafted, Jeweled Gift Boxes, enameled and set with Austrian crystals. Each *Painted Pony* opens and inside there is a secret horseshoe charm. 3" tall and 4" long cast in pewter. 8 Jeweled Gift Boxes are featured in this first collection:

Copper Enchantment	Sky of Enchantment
Happy Trails	Snowflake
Native Jewel Pony	Stardust
Photo Finish	Year of the Horse

. . . .

B *The Trail of Painted Ponies* ornaments have become prized by collectors!

44 Ornaments crafted to date:
(20 Holiday Ornaments & 25 Everyday Ornaments)

Holiday Ornaments:

Big Red (R)	Penguin Express
Christmas Clydesdale (R)	Peppermint Twist
Crystal	Poinsettia Pony
Deck the Halls (R)	Polar Express
Feliz Navidad	Reindeer Roundup
Frosty	Silver Bells
Gingerbread Pony	Snowflake (R)
Golden Girl (R)	Twas the Night Before
Happy Holidays	Christmas
Let it Snow	Wooden Toy Horse
Nutcracker (R)	

D

Everyday Ornaments:

Blue Medicine	Motorcycle Mustang (R)
Boot Camp Pony	Native Jewel Pony
Boot Scootin' Horsey (R)	Patrol Horse (R)
Caballo Brilliante (R)	Quarterhorse (R)
Copper Enchantment	Sacred Reflections of
Dream Warriors	Time
Fetish Pony	Sequential-A Sequine (R)
Fireman Pony (R)	Silverado
Go Van Gogh (R)	Tewa Horse
Happy Trails (R)	Vi's Violet Vision (R)
Karuna (R)	War Pony (R)
Maple Leaf Pony	Woodland Hunter
Medicine Horse	Year of the Horse

. . . .

C Handsome and substantial, these busts make an important statement in any office or home. 9.5" tall and 4.5" long cast in solid resin. 4 Busts have been crafted to date:

Ghost Horse (R)	Thunderbird Suite
Sky of Enchantment	War Pony (R)

. . . .

D Combining the retro-ranch house look with a distinctive style *The Trail of Painted Ponies* lamps will give your home a special glow. 8.5" tall and 17" long cast in resin. 6 Lamps have been crafted to date:

Earth, Wind and Fire (R)	Medicine Horse
Fancy Dancer	War Pony
Ghost Horse (R)	Woodland Hunter

E

F

G

H

I

J

E Pictures of our loved ones can brighten our day and make us smile. Now they can bring a smile to your face in an adorable *Trail of Painted Ponies* frames.
4"x 6" picture frames cast in resin.
4 Picture Frames crafted to date:

Fallen Heroes	*Medicine Horse (R)*
Memorial Pony (R)	*War Pony (R)*
Kokopelli Pony (R)	

F *The Painted Ponies* jigsaw puzzles feature *Painted Ponies* from *The Trail…* discover how much fun games of skill and art can be.
9 Puzzles crafted to date:

Celebration of the '60s	*Kindred Spirits*
Dog and Pony Show	*Northern Lights*
Dream Horse	*Sounds of Thunder*
Great Expectations	*Year of the Horse*
High Desert Horsefeathers	

G Limited edition art prints are perfect for decorating you home or office.
11" X 14"
6 Limited Edition Art Prints:

CowPony	*Lighting Bolt Colt*
Ghost Horse	*Saguaro Stallion*
Happy Trails	*War Pony*

H These attractive coffee or soup mugs will brighten your morning and warm your afternoon. Large 21 oz ceramic mugs.
30 Mugs crafted to date.

• Sandstone coasters make entertaining colorful and effortless.
5 Coasters crafted to date:

Lightning Bolt Colt (R)	*Spirit War Pony (R)*
Motorcycle Mustang (R)	*Thunderbird Suite (R)*
Route 66 Horse (R)	

I These charming note pads will keep you organized when you're on the go...
12 Note Pads created to date:

Blue Medicine	*Medicine Horse*
Fetish Pony	*Silver Lining*
Happy Trails	*Tewa Horse*
Heavenly Pony	*War Pony*
Horsefeathers	*Woodland Hunter*
Kokopelli Pony	*Year of the Horse*

• Pay your bills joyfully with checks from *The Trail of Painted Ponies*.
4 images in this set:

Heavenly Pony	*On Common Ground*
I Dreamed I was a Blue Horse	*Renewal of Life*

J Distinctive plaques add flare to any room.
4 Plaques crafted to date:

Ghost Horse (R)	*Tewa Horse (R)*
Love as Strong as a Horse (R)	*War Pony (R)*

• Magnets make a unique statement!
12 Magnets crafted to date:

Boot Scootin' Horsey (R)	*Patrol Horse (R)*
Caballo Brilliante (R)	*Quarterhorse (R)*
Fireman Pony (R)	*Sequential–A*
Go Van Gogh (R)	*Sequine (R)*
Happy Trails (R)	*Vi's Violet Vision (R)*
Karuna (R)	*War Pony (R)*
Motorcycle Mustang (R)	

• These magical snow globe "wonderlands" will enchant you for years to come!
8 Snow Globes crafted to date:

Christmas Clydesdale (R)	*Nutcracker (R)*
Crystal	*Polar Express*
Frosty	*Silver Bells*
Golden Girl (R)	*Snowflake (R)*

2007

Lightning Bolt Colt featured in *Ride the Sky*

Publishing

With bestselling and award-winning books to its credit, *The Trail of Painted Ponies* is recognized as one of the most prestigious publishers of books on art and collectibles in America.

The Trail of Painted Ponies Collectors Edition books sold through four editions, and with more than 130,000 copies sold, it is one of the most successful "art books" of the last five years.

In 2007 a new side to the ability of *Painted Ponies* to provide people with an inspiring reading experience was revealed with the publication of *Ride the Sky*. This 100-page inspirational book, which pairs dazzling photographs of the most fantastic *Painted Ponies* with uplifting quotations that illuminate a truth embedded in the art, quickly sold through its first printing.

The Trail's most recent book, *American ArtParades: When Pigs Flew, Guitars Rocked and Cows Jumped Over the Moon*, has won national acclaim in the publishing world. This photographic celebration of almost one hundred animal-themed public art exhibitions that stampeded and swam across America is the first book to colorfully chronicle this important chapter in American art history. For this outstanding achievement *American ArtParades* received two major book awards.

In the spring of 2008, it received a Glyph Award from the Arizona Book Publishers Association as Best Book by a New Publisher.

Also, in the spring of 2008, it received an IPPY from the Independent Publishers of America. For 25 years the Independent Publishers book award program has recognized and encouraged the work of publishers "who exhibit the courage and creativity to take chances, to break new ground, to bring about change, not only to the world of publishing but to society." Out of thousands of books that were submitted, *American ArtParades* received the bronze medal in the Pop Culture category.

Look for more award-winning books from *The Trail of Painted Ponies* in the years to come.

2001

2002

2002

2004

2006

Award-Winning American ArtParades!

Bryn Wilkins
Trail of Painted Ponies
Creative Director

"Something extraordinary has happened to American art... it has moved out of museums and paraded right through main streets from coast to coast. Towns and cities have been transformed by bigger-than-life, fiberglass sculptures painted by the best established and emerging artists in the country.

American ArtParades introduces this sensational New American Art Movement to the world. This blast of creativity is truly artful entertainment that has rocked the art establishment and developed an enthusiastic audience that has turned these art parades into a new spectator sport. These exhibitions are innovative, interactive and inspiring, and they have invited people to redefine the very notion of what art is and what art can do."

Excerpt from the Foreward to American ArtParades, by Karlynn Keyes

See this award-winning book in living color and learn how you can support the arts in schools at:
www.americanartparades.com

American ArtParades
Published by *The Trail of Painted Ponies*, 2007

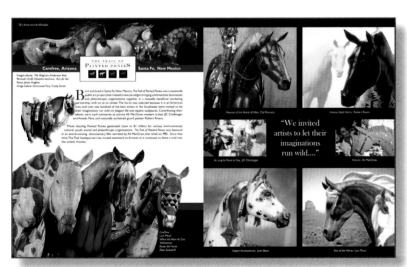

The Trail of Painted Ponies
Featured in *American ArtParades*

GuitarMania   Cows on Parade™   St. Paul's Tribute to
In Chicago   Charles M. Schulz

The Art of Painted Ponies Packaging

When it comes to *Painted Ponies*, art and design are not limited strictly to the contents inside the boxes. Careful consideration has also gone into developing distinctive *Trail of Painted Ponies* packaging.

When the figurines were first released in 2003, they were featured in a glossy black box that was branded with *The Trail of Painted Ponies* logo: the name was featured above four colored horses. Black was chosen for its elegance, and elegance was also what we had in mind when we selected a new burgundy box in 2005.

When it comes to packaging Special Editions of *Painted Ponies* we have enhanced the look with colorful designs. In 2007, the Holiday Ornaments were packed in festive tins, making the container as collectible as the *Pony* ornament inside. Special boxes that reflect the colors and moods of the seasons were also created for each of the Four Seasons Collection figurines.

Starting with the Summer 2008 release of new figurines, we have updated the packaging once again. We retained the rich and recognizable burgundy color and have added pictures of *Painted Ponies* to the front and back of the box. A description of *The Trail* along with the title and the Story Tag for each *Painted Pony* is also featured on the outside of the box.

While some packaging is intended to be disposable once its contents are removed, collectors should take note: *The Trail of Painted Ponies* boxes and Story Tags are perceived to be an important part of the collectibility and value of a figurine.

Painted Ponies Figurine Box
2008

Story Tags
2008

Each *Painted Pony* title and Story Tag are featured on the outside of the box

Front

Back

Four Seasons Collection Box
2008

Four Seasons Collection Story Tags
2008

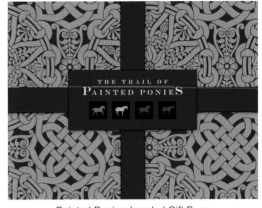

Painted Ponies Jeweled Gift Boxes
2008

Painted Ponies Jeweled Gift Box Story Tags
2008

Painted Ponies Figurine Box
2005

Story Tags
2005

Painted Ponies Ornaments Tin
2007

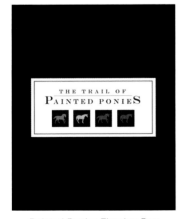

Painted Ponies Figurine Box
2003

Story Tags
2003

Paint Your Own Pony Kit
2005

THE TRAIL OF
PAINTED PONIES

Treasures from the Vault

From its beginning, *The Trail* archived samples of all merchandise created from *Painted Pony* imagery. At some point we intended to make this memorabilia available to our valued collectors, as well as new collectors who missed out on the opportunity to purchase these items when they were originally available. In 2008, we threw open the doors to this collection with a new section on *The Trail of Painted Ponies* website called "Treasures from the Vault."

Featured for sale are early and hard-to-find figurines, rare T-shirts, out-of-print books, our only calendar to-date, solid brass title plaques, and many more items that are no longer available to the public. We also put together collectible combinations and highly desirable sets.

These prized items from the Vault are featured the first of each month exclusively through *The Trail of Painted Ponies Official Website*. Tune in for special online auctions. Details: www.trailofpaintedponies.com

Retired & Autographed *Mosaic Appaloosa* with Collectible Calendar

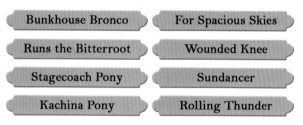

Bunkhouse Bronco	For Spacious Skies
Runs the Bitterroot	Wounded Knee
Stagecoach Pony	Sundancer
Kachina Pony	Rolling Thunder

Solid Brass Title Plaques

Collectible set featuring a Retired *Route 66* Figurine and mirrored turntable

Rare *Snowflake* Snow Globe

Rare *Tewa Horse* Plaque

THE TRAIL OF
PAINTED PONIES

The *Lifestyle Guide*

SHARING THE ART OF LIVING IN SOUTHWESTERN STYLE

*T*he *Trail of Painted Ponies* commitment to "beauty and wonder" in the gift and collectible world has been extended to include a rich mix of merchandise that enhance a lifestyle of creativity and authenticity, all with a classic Southwestern flair.

Included in this ever-growing collection are stunning selections of unique apparel, accessories, home decor and fine art. Coming from *The Trail of Painted Ponies*, we even have something special for your horse to wear!

We invite you to surround yourself with Southwestern splendor.

Directory

Fashion

Horse ♥ Lovers

Home & Ranch Collection

The Trail Gallery

American Collectors Insurance

THE TRAIL OF
PAINTED PONIES

Fashion

From faux-fur jackets, to sparkling fashion jewelry, to casual T-shirts and hoodies, *The Trail of Painted Ponies*-inspired apparel give new meaning to the term "clotheshorse."

A If you love the glitz and glitter of a rodeo, you will adore this fashion jewelry. Austrian crystals and hand-enameling make these pin-pendants extraordinary and the earrings and bracelets sparkle like diamonds.

B There are T-Shirts and then there are *The Trail of Painted Ponies* T-Shirts! Comfortable cotton shirts, ball-caps, and hoodies keep you warm in style. From your home to the ranch, be stylish and comfortable. 21 styles available.

C Gorgeous faux-suede ponchos and jackets feature colorful *Ponies* from *The Trail of Painted Ponies.* Step out in style.

Horse ❤ Lovers

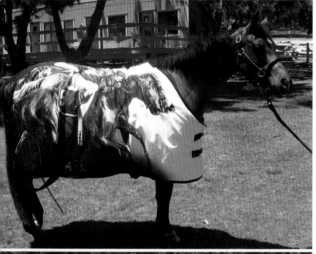

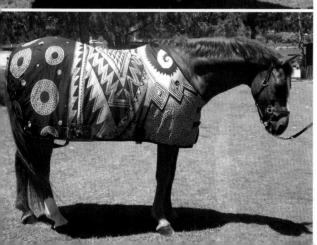

For Horse❤Lovers with a sense of fashion... especially when it comes to their horses.

It's an idea whose time has come: Dress up your horse in a high-quality horse blanket based on a striking *Painted Pony* design.

For years, horse blankets have come in drab solid colors, never getting more exciting than an occasional plaid. That has changed with the introduction of horse blankets from *The Trail of Painted Ponies*. Designed to keep your horse cool and clean in summer, and warm and protected in winter, they are guaranteed to also give it a sense of fashion that will be the envy of the stable!

Check out the choices at: www.trailofpaintedponies.com

Introducing the Equestrian Blankets from *The Trail of Painted Ponies*. Glorious horse blankets and matching halters and leads, make every day at the barn an art experience. 4 styles available.

Series of 4 *Trail of Painted Ponies* Horse Blankets:
Anasazi Spirit Horse, Photo Finish, Wild Women of the West, Crystal

THE TRAIL OF PAINTED PONIES
Home & Ranch
COLLECTION

See how it Feels to come Home to the Ranch

*I*nspired by the look and feel of *Trail of Painted Ponies* art, the *Home & Ranch Collection* was born out of the spirit of the American Southwest.

Special attention is paid to the detail and quality of everything crafted for the *Home & Ranch Collection*. Suitable for that Western lifestyle and home, yet having a style and flair all its own.

Pillows • Throws • Wall Hangings • Bedding • Rugs • Bags • Purses and so much more...

THE TRAIL GALLERY

ART OF THE AMERICAN WEST

The Trail Gallery

*T*he Trail of Painted Ponies occupies an honorable position in the collectible world by virtue of the fact that all of its figurines begin as original, one-of-a-kind, works of art. Many are currently on exhibit in museums, others have become part of corporate collections, or have been purchased by private collectors. We are proud to feature Original *Painted Ponies* by some of the best established and emerging artists in the world and they are available for collectors to purchase. To see all of the original *Painted Ponies* that are currently available, please visit our website: **www.trailofpaintedponies.com**

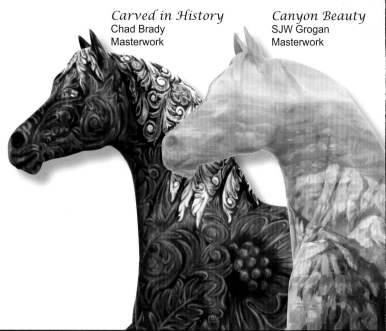

Carved in History
Chad Brady
Masterwork

Canyon Beauty
SJW Grogan
Masterwork

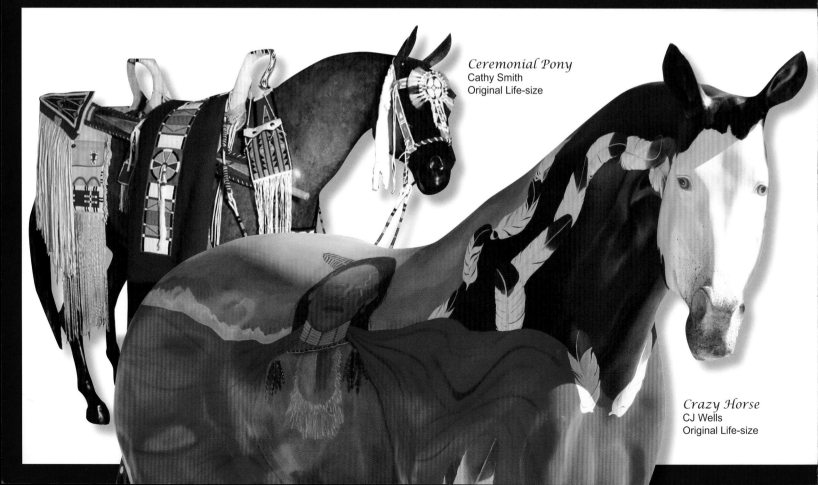

Ceremonial Pony
Cathy Smith
Original Life-size

Crazy Horse
CJ Wells
Original Life-size

Wie-Tou
Barbara Janowitz
Masterwork

Sacred Paint
Gary Montgomery
(Seminole)
Masterwork

Red Nation
Ben Wright
(Cherokee)
Masterwork

Wolf Stands in Snow
CJ Wells

Welcome to the Land of Legends...

*T*he American West is home to some of the finest artists and craftsman in the world and it is our privilege to represent the very best in the west at *The Trail Gallery*.

Many of these artists are distinguished *Trail of Painted Ponies* artists including world renowned painter CJ Wells.

It is our distinct pleasure to work with private collectors and corporations to develop art collections, exhibitions and authentic artistic experiences.

Collect the very best, collect the West!

Please visit *The Trail Gallery* at: www.trailofpaintedponies.com

Collectors & Collections

Nancy Kaufman & Rick Harris

Michelle Ward

Josephine Morrison & Grandaughter

Robin Greene

Mike Cook

Philip Bear

It's difficult to tell you how much my Painted Ponies mean to me. Each horse has a special meaning and a special place in my heart. Marianne, California

I received my first Pony in 2003 as a Christmas gift. I now have 55 Ponies and continue to add to my collection. I'm HOOKED!!!! Tammie, New Hampshire

The Painted Ponies are a very different and a lovely addition to the horse world. Jeannie, Ohio

Gordon Murray

Sandra Dorsey

The Morris Family

Ralph Samples

Bruce Shirley

Kristine Jensen

John & Sandy Stutzman

A Letter From American Collectors Insurance

Dear Collector,

If it's worth collecting, it's worth protecting. American Collectors Insurance gives collectibles the protection they deserve. Collectors invest time, money and passion into expanding their collections, but are possibly still missing something really important -- collectibles insurance from American Collectors Insurance. What many collectors don't realize is that their treasured collectibles may be seriously under insured or even uninsured through their homeowners insurance. American Collectors Insurance, the nation's leading provider of collectibles and collector-vehicle insurance, offers the specialty coverage that collectors need to protect their treasures in the event of a loss and/or damage.

American Collectors Insurance provides insurance for numerous types of collections, including figurines, dolls, teddy bears, vintage toys, model cars, miniatures, collector plates, ornaments, animation art, sports memorabilia, model railroads, vintage advertising, militaria, carousel animals and more. There are so many categories of collectibles, and we provide insurance for most of them.

Most successful companies are born from a desire to fulfill an unmet or underserved need in the marketplace. American Collectors Insurance is no exception. In 1976, the agency established a national program to provide affordable, specialty coverage for collector vehicles. Soon, customers began asking if American Collectors Insurance could protect the "other" things in their garages – namely, automotive memorabilia and petroliana (gas station and auto service memorabilia). It didn't take many of those calls before we started to realize that there were unfulfilled needs in other collectibles markets as well.

Because American Collectors specializes in insuring collectibles, its policies are designed with the needs of collectors in mind and specifically cover perils such as flood, accidental breakage, windstorm and earthquake. $10,000 of blanket coverage can be purchased (in most states) for just $75 per year. Additional coverage is available for collections which exceed $10,000 in value. Claims are paid on an Agreed Value basis, which recognizes collector market value. Scheduled items valued over $2,000 are eligible for inflation guard protection. This feature automatically increases the insured value of the item 2% each quarter of the policy's term. New additions to a collection are also covered automatically; collectors must simply notify American Collectors Insurance of new purchases within 30 days.

One of the keys to American Collectors' success is the wide range of coverage it provides. While it is usually possible to add a floater to a homeowners policy, homeowners insurance is meant to specifically protect the dwelling and its contents. The policy is usually quite limited in its ability to cover collectibles. Even if collectibles are covered by a homeowners policy, the normal exclusions – such as accidental breakage, flood and earthquake – will apply. Also, homeowners insurance will not typically cover collector market value and normally a big deductible - $500 or more - applies.

While inventories are not always required to obtain coverage, American Collectors Insurance strongly recommends keeping an up-to-date inventory in a safe place, since it will be needed in the event of a loss. Collectors who have spent any considerable amount of money on their collections and have seen their collection values appreciate, should protect them, just as they would protect any serious investment. American Collectors Insurance has a reputation for providing superior insurance products, and is also well known for its outstanding customer service and hassle-free application process. Most collectors can easily apply over the phone or online. To apply by phone, collectors can call toll-free (866) 541-6646. Collectors can also apply securely online at: www.AmericanCollectors.com.

Sincerely,

Laura Bergan
Vice President of Marketing
American Collectors Insurance

Artist's Directory

"*Official Trail of Painted Ponies Artists*" are featured in this Artist Directory. The title of "*Official Trail of Painted Ponies Artist*" is given to artists who have been commissioned by *The Trail of Painted Ponies* to paint an original *Painted Pony*. This has become a coveted title and we are very proud to work with some of the finest artists in the world.

A special "Thank You" to all of the talented artists and photographers who have shared their time and talents with *The Trail*!

Adamec, Carol	Campbell, Michael	Garcia, Rick	Jiannine, Joani
Alexander, Ellen	Carpio, Caroline	Gates, Leslie (*Finalist*)	Jirby, Inger
Alford, Jim	Challenger, JD	Gelinas, Katie	John, David K.
Alverson, Steve	Chalom, Matt	Gersch, Wolfgang	Kalayda, Olena
Anderle, Ty	Chan, Jeffrey	Geryak, John	Kaminski, Marcia
Antuna, Rebecca	Chappie-Zoller, Liz (*Finalist*)	Granados, Bernie	Kee, Andersen
Archer, Devon (*Finalist*)	Chelonis, Valerie	Grandjean, Dorothy	Kennedy, Joyce
Auld, Misty Lynn	Chomer, Brett	Graves, Valerie	Kessler, Jennifer
Axton, John	Christensen, Peggy	Greeves, Teri	Keyes, Karlynn
Azbell, Charles	Christie, Nevena	Grogan, S.J.W. (*Finalist*)	Kilhoffer, Kevin (*Finalist*)
Bagshaw, Margarete	Clarke, Joe & Jamie Shene	Guardipee, Terrance	Kimball, Spencer
Baker, Ron	Coffaro, Patrick	Gusterson, Leigh	Kimble, Jason (Mister E)
Bankuti, Denise	Coffin, Doug	Gwinn, Helen	Kimura, Eugene
Barker, Rod	Coonts, Bob (*Finalist*)	Haskew, Denny	Kinkopf, Kathleen
Baron, Bonny	Crabb, Bill	Hassett, Linda	Knauf, Jim
Bean, Lynn (*Finalist*)	Creech, Loran	Higgins, Sharon	Knepper, Vickie
Beason, Pat	Curry, Bill	Hoback, Priscilla	Knox, Grace
Beatteay, Cindy	DeVary, David	Holman, Laurie (*Finalist*)	Krouse-Culley, Nancy
Best, Paula	Dieckhoner, Gene	Hood, Rance	Lack, Del
BlackHorse, Catherine	Dixon, Bill	Hoover, Annetta	LaDell Hayes, Arlene
Blacksheep, Beverly	Dowdall, Mike	Hornbuckle, Marianne	LaMarr
Blake, Bambi	Dryden, Ashley	Horse, Michael	Lampshire, Ross (*Finalist*)
Bonny	Duzan, Barbara (*Finalist*)	Howell-Sickles, Donna	LaRoche, Carole
Bower, Mitzie	Enriquez, Johanna	Hudson, Clarissa	Larsen, Fran
Bradley, David	Escudero, David	Hughbanks, Debbie (*Finalist*)	Leard, Skeeter
Bradley, Judy A.	Esquivel, Dennis	Hughes, Janee	Lemons, Larry
Brady, Chad (*Finalist*)	Espinoza, Noel	Hummingbird, Jesse	Levy, Ben
Briner, B.J.	Evans, Roger	Hunter, Michael, Lorien Cook	Lewis, Lynne
Brown, Barbara	Fields, Anita	Hyde, Doug	Lewis-Scott, Elizabeth
Brown, Denise (*Finalist*)	Fleming, Nancy	Inger, Jirby	Lomayesva, Gregory
Brown, Stacy	Fudenski, Judith	Iron Eyes, Mary	Lopez, Pola
Brubaker, Kay	Gaiti, Ritch (*Finalist*)	Isenhour, Natasha	Losoya, David
Bryer, Diana	Garcia, Connie	Jamison, Tracy	Lowry, Ginger
Burke, LD	Garcia, Letticia	Jimenez, Luis, Adan & Orio	MacGraw, Ali
Calles, Rosa Marie	Garcia, Lydia	Janowitz, Barbara E (*Finalist*)	Machado, Carlos

Artist's Directory

Photographers

MacPherson, Kevin
Magener, Ilse
Marquez, Noel
Marcella
Martin, David
Mattson, Gerri
Mattson, Rich
McGarrell, James
Medaris, S.V. (*Finalist*)
Medina, Gregorio & Graciela
Menchego, Art
Miles, Gino
Miller, Bill
Mitchell Edwards, Jackie
Monfils, Georges
Montgomery, Gary (*Finalist*)
Montoya, Martin
Montoya, Roger
Moore-Craig, Narca
Morawski, Kathy
Morper, Daniel
Morrow, Kathy
Musil, Lori
Nakamura, Joel
Namingha, Arlo
Navaro, Luis
Nelson, Benjamin
Nelson, Bonnie
Newman, Dave
Nieto, John
NoiseCat, Ed
Nordwall, Raymond
Norman, Judy
Nowlin, B.C.
Olguin, Ron
Orr, Chrissie
Ortiz, Virgil
Palma, Israel
Palmore, Lexie (*Finalist*)
Pascal
Patey, Priscilla (*Finalist*)
Payne, Kay (*Finalist*)
Peacock, Cal
Peña, Amado

Peterson, Dorothy
Picavet, Christine
Quick-To-See-Smith, Jaune
Quimby, Barbara
Rabbit, Bill & Traci (*Finalist*)
Ramirez, Joel
Raynes, Jen
Red Star, Kevin
Renk-Mayer, Patrisha
Reyner, Nancy
Ringholz, Amy
Rivera, Robert
Robinson, Emma
Robles, Julian
Robles, Mitch
Roibol, P. Alexander
Romero, Virginia Maria
Rooks, Patti
Rothermel, David
Ruthling, Ford
Ryan, Maria (*Finalist*)
Sabatino, Chuck
Sago, Warren
Sakiestewa, Ramona
Salas, Manuel
Salcido, Frank
Sampson-Files, Cynthia
Sandoval, Ed
Saunders, John
Sawyer, Anne
Schlies, Dianne
Schoebel, Henry Leo
Scripps, Suzanne
Selby, Jeanne
Selden, Lee
Shore, Rick
Silversmith, Mark (*Finalist*)
Sizemore, Sue
Slayton, Mona
Slusher, Carla
Smith, Cathy
Smith, Shawn
Snyder, Janet (*Finalist*)
Sokoloff, Ellen

Speight, JE
Steuerwald, Joy
Stevens, Roderick
Strait, Anne
Strickland, Rabbett
Strongbow, Dyanne
Sweet, Mary
Sykes, Rhiannon
Tammen, Claudia
Tapia, Luis
Tapia, Tom
Tavlos
Thomas-Simpson, Penny
Tivens, Debra
Townsend, Storm
Toya, George
Tubinaghtewa, Buddy
Ulibarri, Dwayne & Ginger
VandenHueval, Michelle
Vanlandingham, Lynn
Vigil, Frederico
Von Eckhardt, Dorothea
Wagner, Jim
Waldrum, Harold Joe
Wang, David
Weese, Susan
Weisman, Scott
Wells-Bailey, Wendy
Wells, CJ
Wening, Karen
Whiting, Wayne
Wiggins, Kim
Willkins, Bryn
Wolfe, Bassel
Wolfington, Aloma (*Finalist*)
Wright, Ben (*Finalist*)
Wyatt, Patricia
Yank, Karen
Yellowman
York, Briana F.
York, Star Liana
Youth of America

Bryn Wilkins
Karlynn Keyes
Valor Lee
Darrell Kosechequetah
Ray Hartl (www.rayhartl.com)
Dave Cruz
Jean-Louis Husson
Bill Manns
Daniel Barsotti
Shelley Heatley
Niman Fine Art
Jack Parsons
LewAlllen Contemporary
Mark Nohl
Margaret Pratt
Marv Shockley
John Guernsey
Leslie Cronin
Jose Rivera
John Wyckoff
Don Bell
Eduardo Fuss

If you would like to learn more about these talented artists and photographers please visit our website:
www.trailofpaintedponies.com

★Artists names featured in RED indicate that they are finalists from *America the Beautiful* and/ or *The Native Art of Horse Painting* Competitions.

Call To Artists

*I*n the way that *The Trail of Painted Ponies* has revealed the versatility of the horse as a canvas that can accommodate a seemingly inexhaustible range of artistic expressions, it has made a major contribution to the art world.

And it continues to provide opportunities for the artistically inclined - known and unknown, young and young at heart - by inviting everyone to download and draw a design on an outline of a horse from the official website (www.trailofpaintedponies.com), or paint a custom Pony from the *Paint Your Own Pony Kit*. Submit your design to *The Trail*'s offices and your *Painted Pony* could be crafted into a figurine!

Submit your design: www.trailofpaintedponies.com

Independent Inspiration
Aloma Wolfington
Walking Horse Form

American Kountry Pony
Maria Jose Guevara
Walking Horse Form

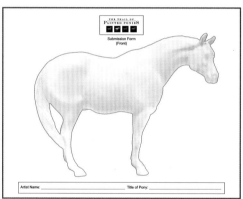

Standing Submission Form

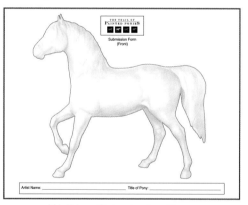

Walking Submission Form

Running Submission Form

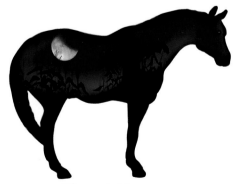

Harvest Moon
Kellie Cook
Standing Horse Form

The Golden Age
Jennifer Lopez
Walking Horse Form

Asleep in the Sleigh
Cheryl A. Harris
Running Horse Form

You Can Be A Trail of Painted Ponies Artist Too!

America the Beautiful Competition and Exhibition
Kentucky Horse Park
Trail of Painted Ponies Artists from left to right: Chad Brady, Kay Payne,
Kevin Kilhoffer with wife Belynda, Lori Musil, Lynn Bean and Ross Lampshire

*T*he title of "*Official Trail of Painted Ponies Artist*" is given to artists who have submitted original designs that have been accepted by *The Trail of Painted Ponies*. These artists are invited to participate in many extraordinary events including exhibitions, competitions, contests, commissions, workshops, signings and special events. It is our privilige to work with some of the best established and emerging artists in the world!

You may be the next "*Official Trail of Painted Ponies Artist!*"
Simply submit your design at: www.trailofpaintedponies.com

Artists from left to right: John Geryak, Olena Kalayda,
Buddy Tubinaghtewa, Gene Dieckhoner

Artist Maria Ryan

Top: Artist Joani Jiannine
Bottom: Artist Chad Brady

Kevin Kilhoffer

Lori Musil, Lynn Bean

Maria Ryan

Ross Lampshire & Laurie Holman

P. Alexander Roibol & Cathy Smith

CJ Wells

The Trail of Painted Ponies, Inc.

Gallery Four Seasons Resort

The Kentucky Horse Park

Special Events & Philanthropy

Just as those who travelled the trails of yesteryear struggled with drama at every turn, so *The Trail of Painted Ponies* is lined with stirring encounters.

Across the land, *Painted Pony* artists have held dozens of *Paint Your Own Pony* workshops, sharing techniques with students - young and old - for bringing Ponies alive with paint. Dozens more are planned, as these gifted artists freely share the enjoyment and rewards that come from painting Ponies.

And just as historic American trails opened up vast new territories to travelers in search of the promised land, so does *The Trail of Painted Ponies* continue to support philanthropic endeavors.

In 2006, the Midwest Chapter of the Young Presidents Organization approached *The Trail* about finding a way of giving back to the state that was hosting its annual YPO conference. An original Masterwork was commissioned and painted by renowned Hopi artist, Buddy Tubinaghtewa. "Moot' y ma" brought $25,000 at the YPO auction, with half the monies going to the Hopi Education Endowment Fund, and half to the winning bidder's charity of choice.

Then, in 2008, to commemorate the 50th anniversary of the Heard Museum Indian Fair & Market, *The Trail* donated four blank Masterworks that were painted by select Native artists and then raffled, raising over $45,000 to benefit Indian student art scholarships.

Doing good, as well as making people feel good has been a part of the fabric of *The Trail of Painted Ponies* since its inception. We will continue to partner with desrving philanthropic organizations.

128

Mooti' y ma
Buddy Tubinaghtewa
Original Masterwork

Young President's Organization

Collector Ed Terry & TAPS Fundraiser

Heard Museum

Romancing the Road
Jesse Hummingbird

Moon Saddle
John Geryak

Dancing with the Moon
Marianne Hornbuckle

Mesa Spirits
Buddy Tubinaghtewa

Celebration of the 60's
Denise Bankuti

Bearback Riders
Maria Ryan

Her Spotted Pony
Judy A. Bradley

Acknowledgements

The Trail of Painted Ponies, Inc.
Cindy Sutton, Rod Barker,
Bryn Wilkins, Karlynn Keyes,
Rikki Lodmell
and the "Ruff Riders"

We are appreciative of… We would like to thank… We owe a tremendous debt of gratitude to... So begins most Acknowledgement sections in books, followed by a roll call of creative spirits who shared the passion from the beginning… generous individuals whose contributions brought a business sensibility to the project… friends who freely gave their time and energy… and family members who patiently put up with the obsessive behavior that is characteristic of every author, every book-maker, committed to producing a masterpiece… under pressure of a deadline. And for everyone who is acknowledged, you can count on the fact that there will be a dozen people overlooked. So why bother?

Because there are people who deserve to be remembered, people without whom this chapter in art history would never have been written. And so we would like to sincerely thank everyone in New Mexico including: Harold and Cris Sternfeld for the introduction of a lifetime, Don Bell, Paul Goblet, Star Liana York, Diane Loomis, Margot MacDougall, Frank Barber, Regina Chavez, Roger and Jill Goldhamer, Jon Nelson, Roger Copple, Eduardo Fuss, Hakim Chisti, Paula MacDonald, Mikki Anaya, Meg Shepard, Bill Manns and Doug and Bobbi Heller.

In Arizona we would like to remember our dear friend and extraordinary artist, P. Alexander Roibol, may he "walk in beauty." Thank you to our real estate broker Mark Crisman, for our beautiful offices. A special thank you to Lori Laramee, our Internet Sheriff. And finally, many thanks to the magnificent design team at *The Trail of Painted Ponies, Inc.* including: Rikki Lodmell, Cindy Sutton and our extraordinary Creative Director, Bryn Wilkins.

A Special Thank You To:

Karlynn Keyes & Rod Barker

This Anniversary Edition book from *The Trail of Painted Ponies* celebrates creativity and compassion. And, like any good anniversary, it honors the passage of time and the spirit of collaboration and commitment. With that in mind, I would like to congratulate my incredible parents, Robert and Anita Keyes on their extraordinary collaboration... Happy 50th Anniversary! Thank you for everything, and more.

Karlynn Keyes
Vice President
The Trail of Painted Ponies, Inc.

❖

"Shyloh, my first horse. I was there at her birth, stroking her, whispering in her ear, blowing softly into her nostrils, hoping to imprint my touch and my scent on her memory for life, without realizing that she was leaving a hoofprint on my heart."

Rod Barker
President
The Trail of Painted Ponies, Inc.

The Artistic Frontier

Every so often something comes along that changes our expectations of what is possible. A new idea. An inspired invention. And it revolutionizes the way we think about ourselves and about the world.

The way *Painted Ponies* inspire each of us to think in terms of our own creative possibilities explains, in part, their popularity. The way they present us with an enchanted and charismatic view of the world and invite us to come along, they do what horses have always done. They provide us with the means for traveling to someplace different. Someplace exotic.

The Trail of Painted Ponies would like to thank everyone for joining us on this ride. And we invite you all to stay in the saddle as we continue our journey on horseback into the artistic frontier.

KEEP ON TRAIL

Happy Trails

We Wish You Happy Trails!

Please visit us at:
www.trailofpaintedponies.com